MAP COLLECTIONS

IN THE

UNITED STATES AND CANADA

A Directory

MARIE CLECKNER GOODMAN
Chairman
Map Resources Committee
Geography and Map Division

1954
Special Libraries Association
31 East Tenth Street
New York 3, New York

INTRODUCTION

This Directory records the map holdings in 527 collections in the United States and Canada. Entries were selected from the more than 1,100 replies received in answer to a questionnaire distributed by the Map Resources Committee to educational centers and private collectors. Those who reported very limited or no map holdings were omitted. The number of collections in the United States is 497; the number in Canada, 30. The arrangement of holdings is alphabetical by state or province.

Information was compiled as reported in the questionnaire. Some research has been undertaken to fill the gaps left by those who returned questionnaires with data missing, or who failed to return them at all. More research would have been time-consuming and it was vital that the material be published while current. The appendix, however, does list depositories of the Army Map Service and the United States Geological Survey which will supplement the entries in the directory.

A few points observed throughout in the presentation of listed material will be helpful to the user:

Certain collections are so comprehensive that no attempt was made to list their area and subject specialties. Such collections are noted at the beginning of the Index.

Most collections specialize to some extent in local maps. Local specialties are not indexed.

For much the same reason, collections in the United States and Canada containing maps of these respective countries are not listed in the index.

Geology, topography and transportation are not indexed as specialties because one out of every four entries includes these subjects.

The Committee hopes that this publication will encourage more libraries and private collectors to report their holdings. Suggestions will be most welcome. The questionnaire which appears in the appendix will serve as a guide for anyone wishing to supply additional data.

1

ACKNOWLEDGEMENTS

Only the generous cooperation of many people has made the completion of this directory possible. Before I mention some of those who worked with me, I must acknowledge the support of the Library of Congress, which with the approval of Dr. Luther H. Evans, aided greatly in the preparation and mailing of the questionnaire. Appreciation is due also to Dr. Arch C. Gerlach, Chief of the Map Division, for his unfailing encouragement and helpful comments.

To my colleagues of the Map Division, particularly Charles W. Buffum and Mrs. Clara LeGear, I wish to express warm thanks for advice and suggestions. Mrs. LeGear initiated the idea of this directory, and with the assistance of Dr. Burton W. Adkinson, Director of the Reference Department, and others, performed much of the preliminary work for the Map Resources Committee.

The Map Resources Committee, of course, deserves special mention. On the Executive Committee were Mrs. Maud D. Cole, of the New York Public Library; Dorothy C. Lewis, co-author of The Classification and Cataloging of Maps and Atlases; Joseph W. Rogers, Copyright Office; and in particular, Kathleen Irish, Army Map Service, who gave freely of her time and talent.

Members of the Advisory Panel included: Nathaniel Abelson, Map Librarian, United Nations; George R. Dalphin, Map Librarian, Dartmouth College; Alexander O. Vietor, Curator of Maps, Yale University; Bill M. Woods, Map Librarian, University of Illinois; Ena L. Yonge, Map Curator, American Geographical Society of New York.

For the aid of the Association of American Geographers, who through Mrs. Evelyn Petshek, helped make certain that data would be forthcoming from all parts of the country, the Committee owes a special debt; and to the following members of the Washington, D.C. Chapter of the Special Libraries Association who helped compile the data, many thanks for the many hours: Hugh Bernard, Sarah Corcoran, Helene Gingras, Barbara Heath, Mary Murphy, Muriel H. Parry, and Mrs. Elsie Yoder.

Marie Cleckner Goodman
Chairman, Map Resources Committee

SPECIAL ABBREVIATIONS

AMS	Army Map Service
exch.	exchange
Iln.	Interlibrary loan available
micro.	microfilm available
not est.	not established
p-t	part-time staff
photo.	photographs available
phst.	photostats available
USC&GS	United States Coast and Geodetic Survey
USDA	United States Department of Agriculture
USGS	United States Geological Survey
Univ.	University
vol.	volumes

ALABAMA

AUBURN

1   Alabama Polytechnic Institute Library.
    Areas: worldwide.
    Serves organization only. AMS depository.

BIRMINGHAM

2   Birmingham-Southern College, M. Paul Phillips Library,
    zone 4.
        Mrs. Margaret H. Hughes, Acting Director.
        Areas: North America.
        Subjects: discovery and early exploration.
        Size: map sheets (14 purchased under terms of the
          Tracy McGregor Americana collections, 1939).
        Serves faculty and students. Iln., commercial phst,
          and micro.

MAXWELL AIR FORCE BASE

3   Air Univ., Cartographic Branch.
        John D. Ashmore.
        Staff: 6; specialists available: geographers.
        Areas: worldwide.
        Subjects: agriculture, air, climate, geology, industry,
          inland waterways, minerals, people, physical, polit-
          ical, railroads, religions, resources, roads, tele-
          communications, topography, transportation, vegetation,
          water supply.
        Size: map sheets 276,500; globes 2; models 25; air
          photos 3,000.
        Serves the Air Univ. Iln., phst., micro.

MONTGOMERY

4   Alabama State Dept. of Archives and History, Map Division.
        Mrs. Hattie M. Allen, Archivist.
        Staff: 1.
        Areas: Alabama and surrounding states.
        Subjects: local history, transportation.
        Size: map sheets 500; atlases 47 vol., 47 titles.
        Serves public.

ARIZONA

PHOENIX

5 Arizona Dept. of Library and Archives, 309 State House.
      Mulford Winsor, Director.
      Staff: 2 p-t.
      Areas: Southwest, Arizona.
      Subjects: local history.
      Size: map sheets 225; atlases 12 vol.
      Serves public. Phst.

6 Arizona Highway Dept., 1739 W. Jackson St.
      Charles I. Smith, Jr., Office Chief.
      Staff: 1 p-t; specialists available: cartographic
        draftsmen.
      Areas: Arizona.
      Subjects: planimetric, topographic, highways.
      Size: map sheets 600; air photos 5,000.
      Serves organization only. Phst.

TUCSON

7 Univ. of Arizona Library.
      Donald M. Powell, Head, Reference Dept.
      Areas: worldwide, Arizona.
      Subjects: various.
      Size: map sheets 9,000 of which 300 are on Arizona.
      Serves organization only. Exch.

ARKANSAS

FAYETTEVILLE

8 Univ. of Arkansas, Geology Dept.
      Contains several thousand topographic, geologic, and
        resource maps, and complete file of folios comprising
        the Geologic Atlas of the United States. USGS
        depository.

ARKANSAS

FAYETTEVILLE

9   Univ. of Arkansas Library.
    Georgia Clark, Head of Reference Dept.
    Grace Upchurch, Head of Loan Dept.
    Staff: 4 p-t.
    Areas: Arkansas.
    Subjects: state history.
    Size: map sheets 24,062; atlases 114 vol., 61 titles.
    Serves faculty and students. AMS depository.

LITTLE ROCK

10 State Highway Dept., P.O. box 2261.
    Fred J. Herring.
    Areas: Arkansas.
    Subjects: state and county highways, traffic flow
       and volume.
    Size: map sheets 500; air photos 10,000.
    Serves organization only. Iln. Phst., blueprints.

CALIFORNIA

BERKELEY

11 Berkeley Public Library, 2090 Kittredge St., zone 4.
    Mrs. Gertrude Reed.
    Staff: 2 p-t.
    Areas: worldwide, California.
    Subjects: topography.
    Size: map sheets 1,513; atlases 68; globes 2. Includes
       1,087 topographic quadrangles and 47 geologic folios
       on California.
    Serves public.

12 Geographische Collectie A.H. De Vries, (private collector)
    Library Bldg., Univ. of California.
    Areas: worldwide.
    Subjects: history of cartography through the ages.
    Size: map sheets 631; atlases 965 vol., 414 titles.
    Serves private study and special classes of Univ. of
       California. The importance of the collection is not
       in the number of items but in their selectness for

CALIFORNIA

12 (continued)
        the purpose of studying map history. Outstanding
        original specimens of different periods of map-
        making are included.
    Publications: Cartographie door de Eeuwen.
    Amsterdam, 1936.

13 Univ. of California, Geography Dept., Map Library.
    John E. Kesseli, Professor.
    Staff: 2; 1 p-t; specialists available; geographers,
        cartographers, translators.
    Areas: Latin America, United States, California.
    Subjects: climate, topography, air photos.
    Size: map sheets 11,400; atlases 150 vol.; globes 4;
        models 8; air photos 6,000.
    Serves faculty and students. Iln., phst., photo.
        through main library, exch.

14 Univ. of California Library, Map Division, Social Sciences
    Reference Service, zone 4.
    Richard V. Teggart, Head.
    Staff: 5 p-t; specialists available: faculty.
    Areas: Pacific Basin, Latin America, Mexico, California,
        San Francisco Bay region.
    Subjects: topography.
    Size: map sheets 68,000; air photos 5,500.
    Serves faculty, students, public. Phst., photo., exch.
        Collection does not include departmental maps; (On the
        Berkeley campus there are also collections in the Ban-
        croft Library, East Asiatic Library, and various de-
        partmental teaching units; geology, geography, forestry,
        paleontology.) Atlases not considered part of map col-
        lection. Unaccessioned map sheets not included in size
        estimate.

    CHULA VISTA

15 William N. Drew, private collector, 291 Davidson St.
    Areas: Southern California, San Diego County, Baja
        California.
    Subjects: various.
    Size: map sheets 1,000. Exch.

CALIFORNIA

DAVIS

16 Univ. of California Library.
    Louise Wheeler, Reference Librarian.
    Staff: 1 p-t; specialists available: translators,
      soil scientists.
    Areas: western United States.
    Subjects: agriculture, soils, geology.
    Size: map sheets 1,787; atlases 55 vol., 37 titles.
    Serves faculty, students, public. Iln., phst.

FAIRFIELD

17 Solano County Free Library.
    Harry M. Rowe, Jr., County Librarian.
    Areas: United States, California.
    Subjects: geology, transportation.
    Size: map sheets 300; atlases 30 vol.; globes 50;
      models 10.
    Serves public and schools. Iln.

FRESNO

18 Fresno State College Library, zone 4.
    Raymund Wood, Senior Librarian.
    Staff: 1 p-t.
    Areas: worldwide.
    Subjects: various.
    Size: map sheets 7,500; atlases 25 vol.
    Serves students, faculty, public. Iln., exch.
      AMS depository.

HOLLYWOOD

19 Paramount Pictures Corp., 5451 Marathon St., zone 38.
    Areas: worldwide.
    Subjects: various.
    Size: map sheets 100 plus 6 file drawers of folded
      maps; atlases 102 vol., 68 titles.
    Serves organization.

CALIFORNIA

LA JOLLA

20 Scripps Institution of Oceanography, Library.
      Specialists available: geographers.
      Areas: worldwide.
      Subjects: hydrography, geodetics, oceanography.
      Size: map sheets 6,200; atlases 40 vol., 21 titles.
      Serves research staff, scientific institutions, univer-
         sities. Iln., ozalid, exch.
      Collection includes USC&GS, USHO, and British
      Admiralty charts, USGS and National Geographic maps.

LONG BEACH

21 Long Beach Public Library, zone 2.
      Staff: 3 p-t.
      Areas: California.
      Subjects: geology, local history, transportation.
      Size: map sheets 4,623; atlases 412 vol., 177 titles;
         globes 7.
      Count includes library branches.
      Serves organization and public. Iln., phst.

LOS ANGELES

22 Los Angeles Chamber of Commerce, Research Dept., 1151 S.
    Broadway, zone 15.
      James H. Lewis.
      Areas: California, Los Angeles.
      Subjects: marketing, population characteristics.
      Size: map sheets 200.
      Serves organization and public.

23 Los Angeles County Museum, Library, Exposition Park,
    zone 7.
      Mrs. Dorothy E. Martin, Librarian.
      Specialists available: historians, geologists,
         paleontologists.
      Areas: Southern California, Nevada, Arizona.
      Subjects: geology, local history.
      Size: map sheets 500; atlases 10 vol.
      Serves museum staff and public. Photo.

CALIFORNIA

LOS ANGELES

24 Los Angeles Public Library, 630 W. 5th St., zone 17.
Anne Mueller, Librarian.
Specialists available: geographers, translators.
Areas: western United States, California.
Subjects: local history.
Size: map sheets 46,538; atlases 806 vol., 492 titles;
globes 2; models 2.
Serves public. Iln. of duplicates; phst., exch.

25 Los Angeles Public Library, Municipal Reference Dept.,
Room 300, City Hall, zone 12.
Ruth E. Palmer, Principal Librarian.
Size: map sheets 163 (state, city and road); atlases
1 vol.; globes 1.
Serves public and Civic Center.

26 Univ. of California at Los Angeles, Bureau of Governmental
Research and the John Randolph Haynes and Dora Haynes
Foundation Collection, 405 Hilgard Avenue,, zone 24.
Dorothy V. Wells, Librarian.
Specialists available: research personnel.
Areas: California, Los Angeles County, metropolitan
area of Los Angeles.
Subjects: local government, economic conditions.
Size: map sheets 1,000.
Serves organization and public. Phst., photo., micro.
Maps partially cataloged.

27 Univ. of California at Los Angeles, Dept. of Geography,
zone 24.
Clifford H. MacFadden.
Staff: 2 p-t; specialists available: geographers,
cartographers.
Areas: worldwide.
Size: map sheets 50,000; atlases 25 vol.; globes 20;
models 30; air photos 100.
Serves Geography and other univ. depts. Exch.

CALIFORNIA

LOS ANGELES

28 Univ. of California at Los Angeles Library, Map Room,
Dept. of Special Collections, 405 Hilgard Ave.,
West Los Angeles 24.
William Bellin, Curator of maps.
Staff: 1; 1 p-t; specialists available: geographers,
historians, translators.
Areas: Pacific Basin, Orient, South Pacific, Latin
America, United States, California.
Subjects: local history, cultural and economic
geography.
Size: map sheets 32,000; atlases 150 vol., 130 titles.
Serves faculty and students. Phst., photo., exch.
Depository for AMS, USGS and USAF.

29 Univ. of Southern California, Owen Coy Memorial Library,
Californiana collection.
Donald C. Cutter, History Dept.
Areas: California.
Subjects: local history, California land grants,
missions, county boundaries.
Size: map sheets 400.
Serves specialists and students. When cataloged, will
be available to qualified students for research on
campus.

MENLO PARK

30 Carl I. Wheat, private collector, 332 Westridge Drive.
Areas: United States, west of 100th meridian,
California.
Subjects: historical development, exploration.
Size: several hundred early maps.
Serves self and interested persons. Phst. commercial.
Collection includes phst. from other collections.
Publications: Wheat, Carl I. Maps of the California
gold region. San Francisco, Grabhorn Press, 1941.

CALIFORNIA

OAKLAND

31 Oakland Public Library, 125 14th St., zone 12.
    Mrs. Josephine Rhodehamel.
    Staff: 1; specialists available: Univ. of California
      faculty.
    Areas: California, Alameda County, Oakland.
    Subjects: local history, California topography.
    Size: map sheets 40,000; atlases 162 vol., 110 titles;
      globes 2; models 1.
    Serves public. Iln., commercial reproductions only,
      exch. Circulating collection limited. AMS and USGS
      depository.

32 Oakland Public Museum, 1426 Oak St., zone 12.
    Staff: 1 p-t.
    Areas: worldwide.
    Subjects: various.
    Size: map sheets 173; atlases 2 vol.; models 2.
    Serves organization and public.

PALO ALTO (STANFORD P.O.)

33 Stanford Univ. Libraries, Central Map Collection,
    Reference and Humanities Division.
    Richard F. Larson, Reference Librarian.
    Staff: 1; specialists available: geographers, carto-
      graphers, translators, science faculty.
    Areas: worldwide.
    Subjects: various.
    Size: map sheets 150,000; atlases 200 vol., 150 titles;
      globes 2; air photos 50.
    Serves faculty, students, visitors. Iln., phst., photo.,
      micro., exch. Special map collections in botany,
      geology and mineral sciences, natural history and
      other depts. All maps holdings will be represented
      in dictionary card catalog in Central Map Collection.
      Reference Manual for the Classification, Cataloging
      and Care of the Map Collection by Neal Harlow and
      Andrew H. Horn (typewritten, 1950) and Library of
      Congress classification schedule G are used.

CALIFORNIA

PASADENA

34 California Institute of Technology, Geology Dept.,
    zone 4.
      Oliver Dunn, Associate Director.
      Robert H. Morrison, Graduate Assistant.
      Staff: 1 p-t.
      Areas: western United States, California.
      Subjects: topography, geology.
      Size: map sheets 12,000; atlases 555 vol., 320 titles;
        models 10; air photos 30.
      Serves faculty and students. Public reference service
        on application. Iln. only on special representation
        of need. Phst., photo., exch.

PORT HUENEME

35 U.S. Naval Civil Engineering Research and Evaluation
    Laboratory, Construction Battalion Center.
      Hope Smalley, Librarian.
      Areas: Alaska, Canada, part of Siberia, Pacific Ocean.
      Subjects: permafrost.
      Size: map sheets 100; atlases 3 vol.., 3 titles.
      Serves organization only. Phst., photo., micro.
        Collection includes USC&GS charts.

RICHMOND

36 Univ. of California Institute of Transportation and
    Traffic Engineering Library, 1301 S. 46th St.
      Beverly Hickok, Librarian
      Staff: 1 p-t; specialists available: aerial photo
        interpreter.
      Areas: United States, California.
      Subjects: transportation.
      Size: map sheets 250; atlases 3 vol., 3 titles; air
        photos 40,000.
      Serves staff and students.

CALIFORNIA

RIVERSIDE

37 Riverside Public Library, 3581 7th St.; P.O. Box 468.
    Staff: Reference Dept. personnel.
    Areas: worldwide.
    Subjects: various.
    Size: map sheets 815; atlases 35 vol., 33 titles;
       globes 1.
    Serves public.   Iln.   Commercial reproductions only.
    Map sheets are indexed, atlases cataloged.

SACRAMENTO

38 California State Library.
    Robert W. Mautner, Junior Librarian.
    Staff: 1 p-t.
    Areas: California, especially counties.
    Subject: history.
    Size: map sheets 18,000; atlases 62 vol., 48 titles,
       plus others in general collections; globes 2.
    Serves public.   Phst., exch.
    Publications: California. State Library. List of Printed
    Maps Contained in the Map Department. 1899.
       Harlow, Neal and Horn, Andrew H.   Reference Manual for
       the Classification, Cataloging and Care of the Map Col-
       lection. 1950.   (Considered for publication by the
       Univ. of Calif.)

39 Dept. of Public Works, Division of Water Resources, Topo-
    graphic Map File, P.O. Box 1079, zone 5.
    Tracy L. Atherton, Topographic Engineer.
    Staff: 2 p-t; specialists available: geographers.
    Areas: California.
    Subjects: topography.
    Size: map sheets 2,000.
    Serves State government.   Commercial reproductions only.
    This is an historic map file of USGS quadrangles of
    California.
    Publications: Biennial Index of Topographic Maps in
    California.

CALIFORNIA

SAN DIEGO

40 San Diego Society of Natural History, Balboa Park, zone 1.
   Mildred H. Hughes, Librarian.
   Areas: California, Lower California, Mexico.
   Subjects: geology, topography.
   Size: map sheets 300 plus USGS folios.
   Serves organization and public. Iln. Collection
      includes state mining publications.

SAN FRANCISCO

41 California State Chamber of Commerce, Research Library,
   350 Bush Street, zone 4.
   Staff: research librarian.
   Areas: California.
   Subjects: soil surveys.
   Size: complete collection of U.S. Soil Survey maps
      of California.
   Serves public. Iln.

41a California State Division of Mines, Dept. of Natural
   Resources, Headquarters Office, Ferry Bldg., zone 11.
   Olaf P. Jenkins, Chief, Division of Mines.
   William A. Sansburn, Librarian..
   Staff: 3 p-t; specialists available: cartographers,
      geologists.
   Areas: California.
   Subjects: geology, mining.
   Size: map sheets 13,000; atlases 300 vol.; air photos
      550.
   Serves public and mineral industries. Iln., phst., exch.

42 San Francisco Chronicle Library, 5th and Mission Sts.,
   zone 19.
   Areas: California.
   Subjects: roads, history, topography, news wirephotos.
   Size: map sheets 3,000; atlases 12 vol.; air photos 150.
   Serves organization only.

CALIFORNIA

SAN FRANCISCO

43   San Francisco Public Library, Civic Center, zone 2.
Dolores Cadell, Reference Librarian.
Staff: Reference Dept. personnel.
Areas: worldwide, Pacific Ocean, western and central
Europe, United States, California, San Francisco.
Subjects: local history, topography, geology, trans-
portation.
Size: map sheets 3,000; atlases 200 vol.; globes 2;
air photos, not est.
Serves public.   Iln., commercial reproductions only,
exch.   No separate map dept.

44   Society of California Pioneers, 456 McAllister St.,
zone 2.
Sybil Power-Kent, Librarian.
Staff: 1.
Areas: Pacific coast, California.
Subjects: topography, overland routes to California.
Size: map sheets 75; atlases 15 vol.
Serves public, and students of California history.
Phst., commercial photo.

SAN MARINO

45   Henry E. Huntington Library and Art Gallery, zone 9.
Leslie E. Bliss, Librarian.
Areas: North America, British Isles.
Subjects: history.
Serves qualified research workers.   Phst., photo., micro.
Representative collection of early maps and atlases.

COLORADO

BOULDER

46   Univ. of Colorado Library, Documents Division.
Areas: worldwide.   AMS depository.

COLORADO

COLORADO SPRINGS

47 Colorado College, Coburn Library.
    Staff: 1 p-t.
    Areas: worldwide, Colorado.
    Size: map sheets 21,400; atlases 150 vol., 135 titles.
    Serves faculty and students. Iln., commercial phst,
    and photo. Collection includes USGS topographic
    sheets and Army War maps.

DENVER

48 Denver Public Library, Civic Center.
    John T. Eastlick, Librarian.
    Staff: 6 p-t; specialists available: geographers.
    Areas: United States, western states.
    Subjects: geology, topography, local history,
    transportation.
    Size: map sheets 7,600; atlases 500 vol., 500 titles.
    Serves public. Iln., phst., Xerograph.

49 U.S. Bureau of Reclamation, Denver Federal Center.
    Mrs. Wilma O'Neill.
    Areas: 17 western states, Alaska.
    Subjects: irrigation, drainage, and canal systems of
    Bureau projects.
    Size: map sheets 3,800.
    Serves organization and public. Iln., phst., photo.,
    exch.

CONNECTICUT

BRIDGEPORT

50 Bridgeport Public Library, 925 Broad St., zone 4.
    Staff: 2 p-t.
    Size: map sheets 15,000; atlases 20 vol., 4 titles;
    air photos, few.
    Serves public. Iln. to local colleges only. Depository
    for U.S. topographic and geologic maps.

CONNECTICUT

BRIDGEPORT

51 Univ. of Bridgeport Library, 400 Park Place.
    Staff: 1 p-t; specialists available: geographers.
    Areas: United States.
    Subjects: history.
    Size: atlases 55 vol., 45 titles; globes 1.
    Serves faculty and students. Iln., phst., Contura.

HARTFORD

52 Connecticut Highway Dept. P.O. Box 2188.
    Areas: Connecticut.
    Subjects: transportation, construction and maintenance
      of highways and highway system records.
    Size: map sheets 200,000; atlases 50 vol.; air photos
      1,000.
    Serves Connecticut Highway Dept., cooperating agencies,
      and public. Phst., photo., blueprints and black and
      white prints for sale.

53 Connecticut Historical Society, 1 Elizabeth St., zone 5.
    T. R. Harlow, Director.
    Areas: Connecticut.
    Subjects: various.
    Size: map sheets 214; atlases 45 titles.
    Serves public. Phst. Collection includes maps of other
      regions when made by Connecticut engravers, printers,
      or lithographers.
    Publications: Thompson, Edmund. Maps of Connecticut
      . . . 2 vol.

54 Connecticut State Library, zone 15.
    Staff: 2 p-t.
    Areas: Connecticut, primarily; secondly, New England.
    Subjects: various.
    Size: map sheets 6,702; atlases 408 vol.; air photos
      11,030.
    Serves public. Phst. AMS depository.

CONNECTICUT

HARTFORD

55 Phoenix Mutual Life Insurance Co., Mortgage Loan Division,
    79 Elm Street.
    W. Roy Wolf.
    Staff: 2 p-t.
    Areas: United States, Canada.
    Subjects: business sections in all principal cities;
      farm land in central and southwest United States.
    Size: map sheets 200; atlases 10 vol.
    Serves organization. Phst., photo.

MIDDLETOWN

56 Wesleyan Univ. Library.
    Richard Anders, Cataloger.
    Staff: 1 p-t.
    Areas: worldwide, Connecticut.
    Size: map sheets 25,000; atlases 450 vol., 400 titles.
    Serves organization and public. Iln. except AMS maps,
      exch. Depository for AMS and USGS.

NEW HAVEN

57 Price and Lee Co., 248 Meadow St.
    Joseph P. Kirby, Production Manager.
    Staff: 1; specialists available: cartographers.
    Areas: cities in Connecticut, New York, New Jersey,
      Massachusetts.
    Subjects: street maps.
    Size: map sheets 56.
    Serves public. Produces and sells city plans.

58 Yale Univ. Library, Map Collection.
    Alexander O. Vietor, Curator of Maps.
    Staff: 1; 2 p-t; specialists available: faculty members.
    Areas: United States and New England.
    Subjects: various, history primarily.
    Size: map sheets 100,000; atlases 2,000 vol., 1,800
      titles; globes 6; models 2; air photos 12.
    Serves organization and public. Iln. atlases only, phst,
      photos., exch.
    Publications: Yale University Catalog and Library (Yale)
      Manual.

DELAWARE

WILMINGTON

59 Wilmington Institute Free Library, 10th & Market Sts.,
    zone 1.
       Areas: Delaware.
       Subjects: local history.
       Size: map sheets 10,772; atlases 97 vol., 92 titles;
          globes 1.
       Serves organization and public. Federal government
          maps available on iln.; Contura reproduction for
          small maps.

WASHINGTON, D.C.

NOTE: see also the following publication:
    U.S. Map Information Office.
       Map Collections in the District of Columbia. Prepared
    by the Geological Survey for the Federal Board of Surveys
    and Maps. Compiled by the Map Information Office, Jan.
    1930, revised and reprinted July 1932, Sept. 1938. Printed
    in cooperation with the National Resources Committee.
       Washington 1938.
          7 p.l., 50 numb. l. 27 cm.
          GA193.U5A5.1938
                    LC 38-26946 Rev.

60 American Automobile Association, Mills Bldg., 17th & Pa.
    Ave., N.W., zone 6.
       Collection includes maps of various types for the use of
       motorists. The AAA publishes and sells road maps at
       nominal prices.

61 Association of American Railroads, Bureau of Railway Eco-
    nomics Library, Room 1002, Transportation Bldg., 17th &
    H Sts., N.W., zone 6.
       Elizabeth O. Cullen, Librarian.
       Edmund A. Freeman, Assistant Librarian.
       Areas: worldwide.
       Subjects: transportation.
       Size: map sheets 1,647; atlases 26 vol.

WASHINGTON, D.C.

61 (continued)
Serves organization and public. Iln., phst., commercial
only.
Publications: Association of American Railroads. List
of Maps Showing Railway Lines. rev. ed. Washington,
D.C., June 1952.

62 Carnegie Institution of Washington, Dept. of Terrestrial
Magnetism, 5241 Broad Branch Rd., N.W.
H. E. Tatel and J. W. Graham.
Specialists available: scientists.
Areas: worldwide.
Subjects: geomagnetism, geology, seismology.
Size: map sheets not est.; atlases 10 vol., 10 titles;
globes 1; also slides.
Serves organization. Phst. Collection consists of pre-
war magnetic charts showing geographical distribution
of the earth's magnetism and its changes with time.
Collection was assembled and maintained chiefly for
use in connection with the survey of the earth's mag-
netic field by land and sea during the years 1904 to
1936. See the Institution's publication no. 578 (1947).

63 Catholic Univ. of America, zone 17.
Eugene P. Willging, Director of the Library.
Staff: 1 p-t; specialists available; geographers, carto-
graphers, translators.
Areas: worldwide, emphasis on United States.
Subjects: various, but more on topography, geology,
soils, vegetation than any others.
Size: map sheets 20,000; atlases 87 vol., 75 titles;
globes 5; models 6.
Serves faculty and students. Micro.

64 District of Columbia Surveyor's Office, District Bldg.,
14th & Pa. Ave., N.W.
Collection consists of atlases, plat books and drawings
utilized in connection with assessments, granting of
building permits, purchases of land, and laying out of
permanent system of highways and of public improvements
in the District of Columbia. Serves public.

WASHINGTON, D.C.

65 Georgetown University, Riggs Memorial Library, 35th & O
    Sts., N.W., zone 7.
    Carol Evans.
    Staff: 1 p-t.
    Areas: worldwide.
    Size: map sheets 50,000.
    Serves faculty and students. AMS depository.

66 National Geographic Society, Cartographic Section, 16th
    & M Streets, N.W., zone 6.
    Mrs. Ruth Maxwell, Map Librarian.
    Staff: 1; 1 p-t.
    Areas: worldwide.
    Subjects: general and sectional topographic.
    Size: map sheets 56,800; atlases 300 vol., 200 titles;
       models, few; air photos, few.
    Serves organization. Collection is used in the produc-
       tion of the maps distributed by the National Geographic
       Society.
    Publications: descriptive folder listing the Society's
       maps available on request.

67 Pan American Union, Columbus Memorial Library.
    Arthur E. Gropp, Librarian.
    Nancy Mango.
    Staff: 1 p-t.
    Areas: Latin America.
    Subjects: agriculture, transportation, communications,
       topography, meteorology.
    Size: map sheets 3,000; atlases 100 vol.
    Serves organization, government agencies, public. Iln.,
       phst., commercial only, photo. and micro. limited,
       exch.
    Books and periodicals analyzed for maps and entered
       in card catalog.

68 Muriel H. Parry, private collector, 2800 Quebec St., N.W.
    zone 8.
    Areas: worldwide.
    Subjects: pictorial maps and atlases.
    Size: map sheets 350; atlases 3 vol., 3 titles.
    Serves collector only. Iln. Collection contains foreign
       and domestically produced pictorial maps ranging from
       maps in travel brochures to wall maps.

WASHINGTON, D.C.

69 The Public Library of the District of Columbia, History -
    Government - Geography Division, Central Library, 8th &
    K Sts., N.W., zone 1.
      Philip J. Stone, Readers' Adviser in Geography.
      Staff: 1 p-t.
      Size: map sheets 1,150; atlases 60 vol., 52 titles.
      Serves public. Iln.; a large number of maps in the
        collection are mounted on linen, folded, and avail-
        able for circulation to public.

70 The Public Library of the District of Columbia, Washing-
    toniana Division Collection, Central Library, 8th & K
    Sts., N.W., zone 1.
      Ethel A. L. Lacy.
      Staff: 1 p-t.
      Areas: District of Columbia.
      Subjects: local history.
      Size: map sheets 583; atlases 87 vol., 20 titles.
      Serves public.

71 The Public Library of the District of Columbia.
    Georgetown Branch.
      The Peabody Library Association maintains a small
    collection of early Georgetown maps in the Georgetown
    Branch.

U.S. GOVERNMENT

72 Aeronautical Chart and Information Service, Air Force,
    Office of Research and Liaison, Research Library Branch,
    zone 25.
      George E. Shepherd, Chief.
      Staff: 30; specialists available; geographers, carto-
        graphers.
      Areas: worldwide.
      Subjects: aeronautical charting.
      Size: map sheets 270,000; atlases 48 vol.; globes 1;
        models 25.
      Serves Office of Research and Liaison, Air Force instal-
        lations, other government agencies. Iln., exch.
      Public sale of aeronautical charts and publications
        is made by the USC & GS.

WASHINGTON, D.C.

73 Army Map Service Library, 6500 Brooks Lane, zone 25.
      Ernest DeWald, Librarian.
      Specialists available: geographers, cartographers,
        translators.
      Areas: worldwide.
      Subjects: topography, city planning, engineering.
      Size: map sheets 1,500,000; atlases 1,200 vol.;
        models 300.
      Serves all U.S. military organizations and other
        government agencies; educational and commercial
        organizations within the limits of military se-
        curity. Iln. within the government agencies and
        on short terms; phst., photo., ozalid, Printon
        (color); exch.
      Publications: Researchers Guide to AMS Library.
      (Technical Manual no. 46)

74 Bureau of Agricultural Economics, Dept. of Agriculture,
      zone 25.
      Elva McCaffrey, Administrative Assistant.
      Staff: 2 p-t; specialists available; visual-informa-
        tion specialists, economists.
      Areas: United States.
      Subjects: economics and statistics.
      Size: photographic negatives of maps and charts; 20,000.
      Serves organization and public. Material not suitable
        for loans. Copies of maps and charts are not already
        made up, but 8x10 inch photographic prints are avail-
        able at nominal charges upon request.
      Publications: U.S. Bureau of Agricultural Economics.
      Agricultural Economic and Statistical Publications,
        June 1952, 83 p.
      _____. Checklist of BAE Publications (monthly.)

75 Bureau of Foreign and Domestic Commerce, Dept. of Commerce,
      zone 25.
      A small collection of maps and atlases has been assembled
    to meet the need in the Bureau for a reference file.

76 Bureau of Indian Affairs, Dept. of the Interior, zone 25.
      A limited file of maps for use in administering the
    Indian Reservations in the United States.

WASHINGTON, D.C.

77 Bureau of Land Management, Dept. of the Interior, zone 25.
Maintains a small collection for administrative use.
During recent years the historical and other maps of interest to the Bureau were transferred to the National Archives
for preservation.

78 Bureau of Plant Industry, Soils, and Agricultural Engineer-
ing, Dept. of Agriculture, Soil Survey, zone 25. Map files
are located at South Laboratory, Soil Conservation Service,
Beltsville, Md.
  J. Kenneth Ableiter, Chief Soil Correlator.
  Soil specialists available for consultation.
  Areas: certain counties and areas of the United States
    and territories.
  Subjects: soils. Maps show the kinds of soil and their
    geographic distribution within the county or area.
  Size: not est. Reports and maps have been published
    since 1899 and cover over 1,600 counties or areas.
  Serves public. Copies of published maps are on file in
    many libraries. For those still in print a limited
    number of copies may be obtained from the Information
    Division, Soil Conservation Service.

79 Bureau of Public Roads, Map Library, Room G-109, General
Services Building, zone 25.
  Mrs. Luella V. Miles, Head, Map Library.
  Stacf: 8; specialists available: cartographers, high-
    way engineers.
  Areas: United States.
  Subjects: transportation - highways in relation to Fed-
    eral and State lands, topography, drainage, and cul-
    tural features. Includes a miscellaneous collection
    of city street maps.
  Size: map sheets 125,000; atlases 30 vol., 30 titles;
    air photos, few.
  Serves organization, other government agencies, public.
    Iln., exch.

80 Bureau of the Census, Geography Division, Suitland, zone 25.
  C. E. Batschelet, Chief.
  Staff: 12; specialists available: geographers, carto-
    graphers.
  Areas: United States, its territories and possessions.

WASHINGTON, D.C.

80 (continued)
    Subjects: Political boundaries of counties, minor civil
    divisions, incorporated places; also boundaries of all
    statistical areas used in Census work.
    Size: map sheets 600,000; atlases 1,800 vol. (Sanborn);
    air photos 300,000.
    Serves Bureau of the Census. Phst., photo., blueprint,
    ozalid; maps can be reproduced only if Census informa-
    tion is shown on them, e.g., enumeration district
    boundaries. No base maps as such may be reproduced
    for the public.
        The Bureau publishes minor civil division maps for
    the states, county outline maps of the states and of
    the United States, and maps showing irrigation and
    drainage basins for certain states. These maps are
    for sale by the Superintendent of Documents.

81 Bureau of Yards and Docks, Navy Dept., zone 25.
    Maintains a working collection of hydrographic charts
    and port plans. Worldwide coverage. For use of the
    Bureau only.

82 Civil Aeronautics Board, Bureau of Air Operations, Tempo-
    rary Bldg. no. 5, wing B, 16th and Constitution Ave., N.W.
    zone 25.
    Anton B. Fabatz, Draftsman.
    Staff: 3 p-t; specialists available; draftsmen and air
    transport examiners.
    Areas: United States emphasized, other areas of world
    to lesser degree.
    Subjects: certified air line routes of the United States;
    foreign air carrier routes.
    Size: map sheets not est.; 10 different maps in series
    and these are corrected as necessary to reflect current
    air routes.
    Serves public. Phst.

83 Coast and Geodetic Survey, Geographic Branch, Charts Divi-
    sion, Map Information Section, Room 1117, Commerce Dept.
    Bldg., Constitution Ave. between 14th and 15th Sts., N.W.
    zone 25.
    Lyman D. Lynn, Chief, Map Information Section.

WASHINGTON, D.C.

83 (continued)
Staff: 5; specialists available: geographers, cartographers.
Areas: United States, its territories, and possessions,
primarily; foreign maps for special projects in which
the Bureau is engaged, e.g., adjustment of European
geodetic surveys.
Subjects: various; the primary purpose of the collection is to have all possible source material for the
compilation of nautical and aeronautical charts.
Size: map sheets 350,000; atlases 250 vol., 200 titles;
models, few; air photos, several thousand.
Serves principally the operating units of the Coast and
Geodetic Survey, and upon request, the federal and
state agencies, and the public. Iln., phst., photo.,
ozalid, exch.
    The Map Information Section also maintains a collec-
tion of 20,000 photographic items, 15,000 of which
have been made into lantern slides for lecture purposes. These are available for magazine and book
illustrations. This collection covers all phases
of the work of the Survey.
Publications: McNeill, John M. Historical Maps and
Charts. Scientific Monthly, May 1940.
Lynn, Lyman D. The Care of Special Materials in the
U.S. Coast and Geodetic Survey Library. Special
Libraries, vol. 31, Nov. 1940.

84 Coast Guard, The Commandant (OAN), zone 25.
Lloyd L. Clay, Nautical Scientist.
Staff: 1; 2 p-t; specialists available; chief quarter-
master.
Areas: navigable waters of the United States, its ter-
ritories and possessions, the Trust Territory of the
Pacific Islands and overseas military bases where the
U.S. Coast Guard has established aids to navigation.
Subjects: navigation.
Size: nautical charts 1,200; atlases 1 vol.
Serves organization. Charts are used for reference pur-
poses in connection with aids to navigation.

WASHINGTON, D.C.

85 Dept. of the Interior, Division of Geography Library, E St.
    bet 18th and 19th, N.W., zone 25.
    Mrs. Elsa S. Freeman, Librarian.
    Staff: 2; 2 p-t; specialists available: geographers,
    cartographers, translators, linguists.
    Areas: worldwide (medium-scale maps showing maximum
    number of place names)
    Size: map sheets 130,000; models 25, air photos 50,000.
    Serves Division of Geography and Board of Geographic
    Names, primarily, the Interior Dept. for nongeologic
    maps, and the public. Iln., phst. for Interior Dept.,
    exch.

86 Federal Communications Commission, zone 25.
    The several divisions have small working collections of
maps on radio, telegraph, and telephone communications.

87 Federal Power Commission, zone 25.
    Leon M. Fuquay, Secretary.
    Areas: United States as a whole, by regions, by states
    and by location of facilities involved.
    Subjects: natural-gas pipe lines, electric transmission
    facilities, and electric generating stations.
    Size: map sheets: several thousand in formal files;
    40 published.
    Serves organization, other government agencies, public.
    Phst. of maps in public files; ozalid prints (of maps
    filed in licensing proceedings that involve hydro-
    electric projects).
    "The maps filed by public (electric) utilities, licen-
    sees and natural gas companies in formal proceedings
    before the Commission are maintained in the files of
    such proceedings. While copies of these and the pub-
    lished maps are available for inspection in the Com-
    mission's offices, they are not maintained in the
    form of a collection."

88 Fish and Wildlife Service, Dept. of the Interior, Room
    5229, Interior Bldg., zone 25.
    William V. Taylor, Chief, Branch of Engineering.
    Staff: p-t; specialists available: cadastral engineers.

88   (continued)
Areas: primarily United States and Alaska; also Canada,
Central and South America and other world areas as
from time to time come within the programs of the Fish
and Wildlife Service.
Subjects: cadastral and topographic surveys; aerial
photography; coast surveys; aeronautical charts; maps
of national wildlife refuges and fish-cultural stations;
breeding grounds; and migration routes of North American birds.
Size: map sheets 18,500; air photos 6,000.
Serves technical, administrative and management activities
of the Fish and Wildlife Service. Phst., photo. Consultation by interested persons is permitted. The Service "makes extensive use of maps, charts, and aerial
photographs in acquiring land for conservation areas;
in the planning, development and administration of conservation areas; in planning and carrying out research
programs in wildlife conservation; and for enforcement
of conservation laws and regulations. Where lands are
being acquired, or where maps are not available from
other sources, cadastral and topographic surveys are
made, and special maps are made to various scales."

89   Foreign Service Institute, Dept. of State, zone 25.
Lloyd D. Black, Professor of Geography.
Staff: 1 p-t; specialists available: geographers,
translators, anthropologists, linguists, economists,
political scientists.
Areas: worldwide.
Size: map sheets 500 plus wall maps; atlases 10 vol.
Serves staff and students only.

90   Forest Service, U.S. Dept. of Agriculture, National Forest
Atlas Records, Room 4244, South Bldg., zone 25.
J. R. McDermott, Chief, Technical Services Section,
Division of Engineering.
Staff: 1; specialists available: cartographers.
Areas: United States, Alaska, Puerto Rico.
Subjects: historical records of the establishment and
growth of the national forests.
Size: map sheets 16,000; atlases 122 vol.

WASHINGTON, D.C.

90 (continued)
Serves the Forest Service; the collection is available
for consultation by anyone. Manual reproduction only
because most maps are overlaid in color. As new issues
of forest administrative maps are available, copies are
furnished cooperative agencies. Very few copies are
stocked in Washington, but instead the maps are stocked
in regional field offices since maps are produced for,
and used as, working tools.

91 Freer Gallery of Art, 12th and Jefferson Drive, S.W.,
zone 25.
Bertha M. Usilton, Librarian.
Specialists available: translators.
Areas: Orient, Far and Near East, South Asia.
Subjects: history.
Size: map sheets 140; atlases 39 vol.
Serves organization and public. Photo.

92 Geological Survey Library, Map Library, Room 1033, General
Services Administration Bldg., 19th and F Sts., N.W. zone 25.
Mark W. Pangborn, Jr., Map Curator.
Staff: 1; 2 p-t; specialists available: geographers,
cartographers, geologists.
Areas: worldwide.
Subjects: geology, minerals, soils, physical, topography.
Size: map sheets 100,000; atlases 1,000 vol., 500 titles;
An extensive collection of air photos is held and ser-
viced by the Map Information Office of the Geological
Survey. (see entry no. 97)
Serves organization, other government agencies, public.
Iln., commercial phst., exch.

93 Hydrographic Office, (Navy) Chart Archives, Suitland, zone 25.
O. M. Nutwell, Archivist.
Staff: 1; specialists available: geographers, cartograph-
ers, translators.
Areas: worldwide.
Subjects: nautical.
Size: charts 34,000.
Serves organization and other government agencies. Iln.,
phst., photo., photo-lith.

WASHINGTON, D.C.

94   International Boundary Commission, United States, Alaska,
      and Canada, Room 1029, 101 Indiana Ave., N.W., zone 25.
      Areas: Canada and the United States, and Alaska and
      Canada adjacent to the international boundary line.
      Size: Collection includes 216 maps made by the Commis-
      sion in carrying out the Provisions of the Treaties
      of 1903, 1906, 1908, and 1910 regarding the demarca-
      tion of the international boundary. Map sheets are
      available for distribution.

95   Interstate Commerce Commission, Bureau of Valuation, 12th
      and Constitution Ave., N.W., zone 25.
         John E. Hansbury, Acting Director.
         Areas: United States.
         Subjects: railroads and pipe lines.
         Size: map sheets 400,000.
         Serves organization only. Phst. Maps were collected
         in connection with valuation of common-carrier rail-
         roads and pipe lines subject to the jurisdiction of
         the ICC.

96   Library of Congress, Map Division, zone 25.
         Arch C. Gerlach, Chief.
         Staff: 17; specialists available: geographers, histori-
         cal and technical cartographers, map librarians,
         translators.
         Areas: worldwide, comprehensive, including all avail-
         able editions.
         Subjects: various, comprehensive.
         Size: map sheets 2,250,000; atlases 18,500 vol., 10,000
         titles, globes 125; models 150.
         Serves Congress, other government agencies, public. Iln.,
         phst., photo., ozalid, micro., kodachrome; exch.
         Publications:
            "Annual Report of Acquisitions of the Map Division"
         regularly included in the August issue of the Library
         of Congress Quarterly Journal of Current Acquisitions.
            The Hotchkiss Map Collection, a List of Manuscript
         Maps, Many of the Civil War Period, prepared by Major
         Jed. Hotchkiss, and Other Manuscript and Annotated Maps
         in his Possession. Compiled by Clara Egli LeGear, with
         a foreword by Willard Webb. Washington, 1951.

WASHINGTON, D.C.

96   (continued)
The Kohl Collection (now in the Library of Congress)
of Maps Relating to America. By Justin Winsor. A re-
print of Bibliographical Contribution number 19 of the
Library of Harvard University. With index by Philip
Lee Phillips. Washington, Govt. Print. Off., 1904.
A List of Geographical Atlases in the Library of Con-
gress, with Bibliographical notes, by Philip Lee
Phillips. Washington, Govt. Print. Off., 1909-20. 4 vol.
List of Maps and Views of Washington and District of
Columbia in the Library of Congress, by P. Lee Phillips.
Washington, Govt. Print. Off., 1900. (56th Cong., 1st
sess. Senate Doc., 154)
A List of Maps of America in the Library of Congress,
preceded by a List of Works Relating to Cartography, by
P. Lee Phillips. Washington, Govt. Print. Off., 1901.
The Lowery Collection. A Descriptive List of Maps of
the Spanish Possessions Within the Present Limits of
the United States, 1502-1820. Ed. with notes by Philip
Lee Phillips. Washington, Govt. Print. Off., 1912.
Map Division. Washington, 1950. (Departmental and
Divisional Manuals, no. 15)
Maps: their Care, Repair and Preservation in Libraries,
by Clara Egli LeGear. Washington, 1950.
Marketing Maps of the United States, an Annotated
Bibliography; 2d. rev. ed., by Marie C. Goodman and
Walter W. Ristow. Washington, 1952.
The Services and Collections of the Map Division, by
Walter W. Ristow, 1951.
Three-Dimensional Maps; an Annotated List of References
Relating to the Construction and Use of Terrain Models,
compiled by Walter W. Ristow. Washington, 1951.
United States Atlases; a List of National, State, City
and County, Regional Atlases in the Library of Congress,
by Clara Egli LeGear. Washington, 1950-53. 2 vol.

97   Map Information Office, U.S. Geological Survey, F St.,
between 18th and 19th, N.W., zone 25.
J. O. Kilmartin, Chief.
Staff: 6; specialists available: cartographers.
Areas: United States, territories and Island possessions.

97 (continued)
    Subjects: topography.
    Size: map sheets 30,000; air photos 4,000 (indexes).
    Serves public. Iln., phst., photo., reflex prints, film
    postive or negative; exch. The Map Information Office
    is a clearing house for information pertaining to the
    mapping activities of all Federal agencies. Records
    are maintained and index maps are issued periodically
    showing the status of topographic mapping, aerial
    photography, aerial mosaics, horizontal and vertical
    control in the United States, its territories and
    Island possessions.

98 National Archives, Cartographic Records Branch, 8th and
    Pa. Ave., N.W., zone 25.
    Herman R. Friis, Chief Archivist.
    Staff: 8; specialists available; geographers, carto-
    graphers, translators, historians, economists,
    political scientists.
    Areas: worldwide, but emphasis on North America.
    Subjects: various, representing the official activities
    of the Federal Government.
    Size: map sheets 800,000; atlases 250 vol.; survey
    field notes 2,500; air photos available in Audio-
    Visual Records Branch.
    Serves organization, Federal government, public. Iln.
    restricted to Federal agencies; phst., photo., micro.,
    ozalid, lantern slides. The cartographic and related
    records in the Cartographic Records Branch are those
    map records of the Federal Government which because of
    their continuing legal, administrative and historical
    value must be retained permanently. They are first
    appraised in the agency and then transferred to the
    National Archives in accordance with certain specific
    procedures and are retained, arranged, and serviced
    as the permanent records of the creating or issuing
    agency. They are therefore not interfiled or arranged
    as one large collection but rather continue to exist
    as the separate, individual group of records of the
    agency. The records now in the Branch represent units
    of about 85 different mapping and map-using agencies
    of the Federal government, some of which are no longer

WASHINGTON, D.C.

98   (continued)
        in existence. A centralized control in the form of
        card catalogs, descriptive lists, inventories and map
        and graphic indexes is maintained in the Branch's
        Search Room. About two-thirds of the holdings are
        manuscript, annotated maps covering the period 1775
        to date although a few reflect earlier dates.
     Publications: Preliminary Inventories of the Carto-
        graphic Records of the Federal Housing Administration
        (Record Group 31) compiled by Charlotte Munchmeyer.
        Washington, 1952. (National Archives Preliminary In-
        ventories no. 45) 57 p. multilith, map. In prepara-
        tion: several special finding lists, catalogs, and
        inventories of one or more groups (collections) of
        maps. A Guide to the Records in the Cartographic
        Records Branch in the National Archives is planned
        for publication in the Fall 1953.

99   National Capital Parks and Planning Commission, Interior
     Bldg., zone 25.
        Sizable collection of maps, drawings and plans relating
     to the Commission's city and regional planning program
     for the National Capital and its environs, including parts
     of Maryland and Virginia.

100 National Park Service, Dept. of the Interior, zone 25.
        Charles A. Richey, Chief of Lands.
        Areas: national parks, monuments, and other areas ad-
           ministered by the National Park Service in the United
           States, Hawaii and Alaska.
        Subjects: cultural and physical features of the areas.
        Size: map sheets 150.
        Serves organization and public. Maps available for
           public distribution. Phst.

101 National War College Library, zone 25.
        F. E. Fitzgerald, Librarian.
        Areas: worldwide.
        Subjects: various.
        Size: map sheets, not. est.; atlases 143 vol., 125 titles;
           globes 1.
        Serves organization only. Phst., photo.

WASHINGTON, D.C.

102   Office of Foreign Agricultural Relations, Dept. of Agriculture, zone 25.
R. G. Hainsworth, Geographer.
Areas: Europe, Asia, Latin America.
Subjects: topographic features.
Size: map sheets, several hundred; atlases 2 titles.
Serves organization only. Collection is a reference
tool closely connected with the work of the Office.

103   Office of the Chief of Engineers, Dept. of the Army, zone 25.
A collection of maps, plans, and drawings on civil works
and military construction. For administrative use.

104   Post Office Dept., Division of Topography, zone 25.
Has on file post route maps and rural delivery maps
(both county and local). The Dept. publishes maps primarily for use of the Postal Service but copies are available to the public at nominal cost. Price list upon
request.

105   Production and Marketing Administration, Dept. of Agriculture, zone 25.
Ralph H. Moyer, Chief, Aerial Photographic and Engineering Service.
Areas: 70 percent of the land area of the United States.
Size: 1,428,000 aerial negatives covering nearly 2,500,000
square miles. The Service has also prepared aerial mosaics of some areas in the United States.
Serves public. Projections from negatives are available
at various scales for nominal prices.

106   Rural Electrification Administration, U.S. Dept. of Agriculture, zone 25.
Maps are part of the administrative files and reports on
the distribution of electric power.

107   Smithsonian Institution Library, National Museum Bldg.,
10th and Constitution Ave., N.W., zone 25.
Specialists available: geologists.
Areas: Latin America, United States.
Subjects: geology.

WASHINGTON, D.C.

107 (continued)
    Serves scientists and staff. No separate map collection.
    A few maps are kept with the general atlases. An al-
    most complete set of USGS topographic maps are filed
    in the Dept. of Geology. A set of the millionth map
    of South America is filed in the Division of Mammals.

108 Weather Bureau, Library, 24th & M Sts., N.W., zone 25.
    R. C. Aldredge, Librarian.
    Staff: 1 p-t.
    Areas: worldwide.
    Subjects: meteorology.
    Size: atlases 3,900 vol., 52 titles.
    Serves public. Iln., phst., micro. One of largest col-
    lections of daily weather charts. The Bureau issues a
    daily weather map which shows the weather observed at
    1:30 a.m. EST by approximately 400 stations. The map
    is available on a subscription basis.

FLORIDA

CORAL GABLES

109 Univ. of Miami, Geography Dept., Map Library, zone 46.
    Richard D. Kreske, Associate Professor of Geography.
    Staff: 2 p-t; specialists available: geographers,
    cartographers, translators.
    Areas: worldwide with some emphasis on Latin America
    and Florida.
    Subjects: various.
    Size: map sheets 30,000; atlases 120 vol., 20 titles;
    globes 50; models 150; air photos 1,000.
    Serves university and public. Iln., phst., photo.

GAINESVILLE

110 Florida Historical Society Library, Box 3645, Univ. Station.
    Edward C. Williamson, Librarian.
    Staff: 1 p-t; specialists available: geographers, carto-
    graphers, translators.
    Areas: Florida.

FLORIDA

110 (continued)
        Subjects: history.
        Size: map sheets 700; atlases 6.
        Serves organization and public. Phst., photo.

        TALLAHASSEE

111 Mark F. Boyd, private collector, 615 East 6th Ave.,
        Areas: Florida.
        Size: map sheets 209; air photos, several.
        Loan privileges to Univ. of Miami, others by appoint-
            ment only; exch., commercial reproductions only.
        Maps are part of collection of Floridiana. Total
            number given is exclusive of quadrangle sheets of
            USGS, county soil surveys and coast charts; neither
            does this total include books containing significant
            maps not available in other form, of which there are
            30.

112 Florida State Univ. Library.
        Estelle Ardrey, Map Librarian.
        Staff: 1; 3 p-t; specialists available: geographers,
            cartographers, translators.
        Areas: southeastern United States, Florida.
        Subjects: local history.
        Size: map sheets 50,000; atlases 100 vol., 90 titles;
            globes 1; models 1.
        Serves faculty, students, public. Iln., phst., exch.

113 State Road Dept. of Florida.
        Charles E. Gray, Assistant Engineer of Traffic and
            Planning.
        Staff: 10; 10 p-t; specialists available: cartographers,
            translators.
        Areas: Florida.
        Subjects: transportation.
        Size: map sheets on 67 counties.
        Serves public. Phst., blueprints, ozalid, blue line
            prints, lithoprints. Price list available.

GEORIA

The publication noted below indicates the ownership of
Georgia maps by departments of the State Government:

Classified Inventory of Georgia Maps. Prepared by
Georgia Historical Records Survey (and others).
East Point, Georgia, Georgia State Planning Board,
April 1941. 150 p.

ATHENS

114 Univ. of Georgia, Dept. of Geography and Geology, Map
Collection.
James A. Barnes, Assistant Professor.
Staff: p-t; specialists available: geographers,
cartographers.
Areas: worldwide, United States, southeastern United
States.
Subjects: topography, geology.
Serves faculty, students, public. Limited iln., com-
mercial reproductions. The Historical Map Collection
and this dept. collection together total 100,000 map
sheets.

115 Univ. of Georgia Libraries, Historical Map Collection.
John W. Bonner, Jr., Head, Special Collections.
Staff: p-t.
Areas: the South, Georgia.
Subjects: local history.
Serves faculty, students, public. Limited iln., com-
mercial reproductions. The Historical Map Collection
and the Map Collection in the Dept. of Geography and
Geology together total 100,000 map sheets.

ATLANTA

116 Atlanta Public Library, 126 Carnegie Way, N.W., zone 3.
Areas: United States, Georgia, Atlanta.
Subjects: local history, cities over 100,000 population.
Size: map sheets 150; atlases 90 vol., 63 titles;
globes 2.
Serves public. Iln., phst. and photo. available com-
mercially.

GEORGIA

ATLANTA

117 Georgia Institute of Technology Library, 225 North Ave., N.W.
     Miss Safford Harris, Documents Librarian.
     Staff: 1; specialists available: 1 geographer.
     Areas: southeastern United States.
     Subjects: geology, architecture, city planning, trans-
        portation.
     Size: map sheets 21,443; atlases 567 vol., 236 titles;
        globes 2.
     Serves students, faculty, research staff of Engineering
        Experiment Station, research scholars, citizens of
        Georgia. Phst., photo., micro., exch.

118 State Highway Dept. of Georgia, Division of Highway Plan-
     ning, 2 Capitol Square, zone 3.
     Roy A. Flynt, State Highway.Planning Engineer.
     Specialists available: cartographers, highway engineers.
     Areas: Georgia.
     Subjects: highway transportation.
     Size: map sheets 160.
     Serves organization, government agencies, public. Pub-
        lished maps for sale; commercial blueprints. Collec-
        tions consists of state highway map and individual
        road maps of the 159 counties.

119 Univ. of Georgia, Atlanta Division Library, 24 Ivy St., S.E.
     Wilson Noyes, Jr., Librarian.
     Areas: scattered, primarily United States.
     Size: map sheets 100; atlases 23 vol., 17 titles;
        globes 1.
     Serves faculty and students. Iln., exch.

SAVANNAH

120 Georgia Historical Society, 501 Whitaker St.
     Mrs. Lilla M. Hawes, Director.
     Areas: Georgia, Savannah.
     Subjects: local history.
     Size: map sheets 1,158 plus; atlases 9.
     Serves public. Phst.

HAWAII

HONOLULU

121   Bernice P. Bishop Museum, zone 17.
      Edwin H. Bryan, Jr., Curator of Collections.
      Margaret Titcomb, Librarian.
      Staff: 1 p-t.
      Areas: southeastern and eastern Asia, Pacific Islands,
         shores of the Pacific.
      Serves museum staff, scientists in Hawaii, limited
         public. Commercial phst.

122   U.S. Geological Survey, Water Resources Division, 333
      Federal Bldg., zone 13.
      D. A. Davis.
      Areas: Pacific Ocean.
      Subjects: topography, geology, hydrology.
      Size: map sheets 200.
      Serves organization and public.

123   Univ. of Hawaii Library, zone 14.
      Mrs. Clora Ching, Library Assistant in Charge of Map
         Collection.
      Staff: 1; specialists available: geographers, trans-
         lators, faculty.
      Areas: Pacific Ocean.
      Subjects: topography, local history.
      Size: map sheets 31,802; atlases 68 vol., 63 titles;
         globes 1.
      Serves faculty, students, public. Micro. AMS depository.
      Collection almost completely cataloged.

IDAHO

BOISE

124   Idaho State Historical Dept., 610 Parkway Drive.
      Areas: Lewis and Clark routes, Indian reservations,
         Idaho.
      Subjects: history, highways, mining, forests.

IDAHO

MOSCOW

125   Univ. of Idaho Library.
      Charles A. Webbert, Reference Librarian.
      Specialists available: geographers.
      Areas: Pacific Northwest, Idaho.
      Subjects: local history.
      Size: map sheets 52,700; atlases 72 vol., 60 titles;
         globes 1; models 1.
      Serves faculty, students, public.

ILLINOIS

AURORA

126   Aurora Historical Society, Map Collection, 304 Oak Ave.
      Alice H. Applegate, Curator.
      Staff: 1 p-t.
      Areas: northwest Territory, Aurora and vicinity.
      Subjects: local history.
      Size: map sheets 76 (including 25 large wall maps);
         atlases 8 vol., 8 titles; globes 1; air photos 7.
      Serves organization and public.   Photo.

CARBONDALE

127   Southern Illinois Univ. Libraries, Reference Division.
      Staff: p-t; specialists available: geographers, geo-
         logists.
      Size: map sheets 33,560; globes 2.
      Serves faculty and students.   Phst., micro., exch.
      AMS depository; USGS maps.   Plan to build specialized
         collection on Southern Illinois.

CHICAGO

128   Chicago Historical Society, North Ave and Clark St, zone 14.
      Margaret Scriven, Librarian.
      Staff: 1 p-t.
      Areas: Illinois, Chicago.
      Subjects: local history, transportation, Civil War.
      Size: map sheets 5,000; atlases 675 vol.
      Serves organization and public.   Phst., photo., micro.

ILLINOIS

CHICAGO

129 Chicago Public Library, 78 E. Washington st., zone 2.
      Irene H. Peterson, Chief, Business and Civics Dept.
      Areas: worldwide.
      Staff: 2 p-t.
      Size: map sheets 15,613; atlases 23 vol.
      Serves public. Phst., depository for U.S. government
        topographic and soil maps. Have street maps of
        many U.S. cities.

130 Denoyer-Geppert Company, Editorial Dept., 5235 N.
      Ravenswood, zone 40.
        C. B. Odell, Managing Editor.
        Staff: 1 p-t; specialists available: geographers,
          cartographers, translators.
        Areas: worldwide.
        Subjects: various.
        Size: map sheets 7,000; atlases 175 vol., 150 titles;
          globes 20.
        Serves organization. Iln., exch. Special collection
          of small school atlases by U.S. and foreign publishers.
          Manuscript handbook on filing system and use of col-
          lection available to users.

131 Godfrey J. Eyler, private collector, McCall's Western
      Advertising Office, 919 N. Michigan Ave., zone 11.

132 Foote, Cone & Belding, 155 E. Superior St., zone 11.
      Patricia Finley, Librarian.
      Areas: United States.
      Subjects: street maps of major cities.
      Size: map sheets 200; atlases 1.
      Serves organization.

133 John Crerar Library, 86 E. Randolph St., zone 1.
      Specialists available: translators.
      Areas: worldwide.
      Subjects: geology, engineering, agriculture, transpor-
        tation and communications.
      Serves public. Iln., phst., photo., micro. Contains
        complete set USGS maps, lake maps, soil survey maps
        and scattered state Geological Survey maps.

ILLINOIS

CHICAGO

134   Municipal Reference Library, Room 1005, City Hall, zone 2.
       Frederick Rex, Librarian.
       Areas: Chicago.
       Subjects: local history.
       Size: atlases 25 vol.
       Serves public.   Iln., phst.

135   Newberry Library, 60 W. Walton, zone 10.
       Mrs. Ruth Lapham Butler, in charge of the Ayer Collection.
       Staff: 1 p-t.
       Areas: worldwide.
       Subjects: local history, travel, exploration, develop-
          ment of the United States and of colonial Latin America.
       Size: map sheets 375 plus AMS and USGS topographic sets;
          atlases 385 vol.
       Serves persons doing advanced historical research.   Iln.
          Newberry has a Contura camera with which it can provide
          sub-professional reproductions of limited size; other-
          wise materials are sent to the University of Chicago
          or to a professional company.   AMS depository.
             Newberry's collection of charts and maps of early
          American travel and exploration, while not large, is
          important for its scholarly and historical significance.
          It contains several editions of Ptolemy, a number of
          portolans, and the Karpinski collection of photofac-
          similes of early maps of the Americas taken from French
          and Spanish archives.
             Mercator and Ortelius atlases are in the collection,
          as well as a number of maps and charts of early United
          States travel and exploration.   These materials are
          largely in the Ayer Collection.

136   A. J. Nystrom & Co., 3333 Elston Ave., zone 18.
       Robert E. Daehn, Assistant Editor.
       Staff: 1 p-t; specialists available: geographers, carto-
          graphers.
       Areas: Latin America, Europe, Wisconsin, Illinois.
       Subjects: physical and regional geography.

ILLINOIS

136 (continued)
     Size: map sheets 5,000; atlases 150 vol., 150 titles;
         globes 10; air photos, few.
     Serves editorial dept. and answers questions received
         from customers.

137 Rand McNally & Company, Library, Cartographic Research
     and Production, Box 7600, zone 80.
     Carl H. Mapes, Chief Map Editor.
     Staff: 5 p-t; specialists available: geographers,
         cartographers, translators.
     Areas: worldwide, United States, Canada.
     Subjects: transportation, topography.
     Size: map sheets 25,000-30,000 (active files);
         atlases 500 vol., 400 titles.
     Serves organization and subscribers to Commercial
         Atlas Service, Phst.

138 Univ. of Chicago, Map Library, Rosenwald Hall.
     Agnes Whitmarsh, Map Librarian.

139 Univ. of Illinois Library, Chicago Undergraduate Division,
     Navy Pier, zone 11.
     Staff: 2 p-t; specialists available: faculty.
     Areas: Illinois, Chicago.
     Subjects: geology.
     Size: map sheets 3,250; atlases 80 vol., 70 titles;
         globes 1.
     Serves faculty, students, public. Iln. (atlases only).

CHICAGO HEIGHTS

140 Weber Costello Company.
     W. F. Scarborough, Director of Maps and Globes.
     Areas: worldwide.
     Subjects: geography, history.
     Size: map sheets 400; atlases 10 vol.; globes 50.
     Serves organization. Collection contains reference
         information for publishing maps and globes.

ILLINOIS

EVANSTON

141 Northwestern Univ. Library, Map Library.
Tracy V. Robb, Map Librarian.
Staff: 1 p-t; specialists available: geographers,
cartographers.
Areas: worldwide, United States, Canada, Great Britain.
Subjects: various.
Size: map sheets 60,000 (including duplicates); atlases
120 vol., 110 titles.
Serves faculty, students, public, map companies in the
Chicago area. Iln., phst., commercial, micro., exch.
Publications: Northwestern Library News, II, 45,
August 6, 1948; III, 16, Jan. 14, 1949; IV, 27,
March 31, 1950; V, 16, Jan. 12, 1951.

GALESBURG

142 Galesburg Public Library, S. Broad St. at Simmons.
Margaret Maltby, Cataloger.
Staff: 1 p-t.
Areas: Illinois.
Subjects: United States geology, local history.
Size: atlases 240 vol. (Illinois counties)
Serves public. Phst.

143 Knox College, Geography Dept.
A. C. Walton, Professor.
Specialists available: cartographer, translator.
Subjects: local history of the Southwest; general
collection for teaching purposes.
Size: map sheets 300; atlases 14 vol., 8 titles;
globes 8; models 20; air photos 100.
Serves students. Visitors permitted to take photos.
Collection is for teaching purposes only.

ILLINOIS

LAKE FOREST

144 Hermon D. Smith, private collector, 121 Stone Gate Road.
     Areas: Great Lakes area, Illinois.
     Subjects: maps prior to 1850.
     Size: map sheets 100; atlases 10 vol., 10 titles. Iln.
     Collection includes many maps of United States, es-
     pecially of the Middle West, issued as part of 18th
     and 19th Century travel books.

NORMAL

145 Illinois State Normal Univ., Milner Library.
     Eleanor Weir Welch, Director of Libraries.
     Specialists available: geographers, cartographers,
        translators, faculty.
     Areas: United States, Illinois.
     Size: map sheets 18,500; atlases 40; globes 3.
     Serves faculty, students and public. Phst.

PEORIA

146 Bradley Univ., Map Center, Library 308.
     E. Heyse Dummer, Director of the Library.
     Specialists available: geographers, translators.
     Areas: worldwide.
     Size: map sheets 20,000; atlases 34 vol., 34 titles.
     Serves faculty and students. AMS depository.

147 Peoria Public Library, 111 N. Monroe St.
     Areas: United States, Peoria.
     Size: map sheets 150 plus USGS collection; atlases
        80; globes 1.
     Serves public. Iln., except current atlases. Com-
     mercial reproductions only. Depository for USGS
     topographic maps.

ILLINOIS

ROCK ISLAND

148 Augustana College Library, Reference Dept.
     Staff: 1 p-t; specialists available: geographers,
        geologists.
     Size: map sheets 10,000; atlases 40 vol., 40 titles;
        globes 1.
     Serves faculty and students. AMS depository; USGS maps.

SMITHSHIRE

149 Charles Frederick Strong, private collector, RFD #1.
     Areas: worldwide, United States, southwest United
        States.
     Subjects: 19th & 20th Century atlas cartography.
     Size: map sheets 400; atlases 200 vol., 175 titles;
        globes 2; air photos 4. Exch. Collection includes
        historical, school and hand atlases, and land use
        maps.

SPRINGFIELD

150 Illinois Division of Highways, Bureau of Research and
     Planning, 126 E. Ash St.
     W. L. Esmond, Engineer of Research and Planning.
     Staff: 1; specialists available: cartographers.
     Areas: Illinois.
     Subjects: highway transportation.
     Size: map sheets 100.
     Serves Illinois Division of Highways and other govern-
        mental and private agencies. Planograph and blue
        line prints.

151 Illinois State Historical Library, Centennial Building.
     Staff: 2 p-t.
     Areas: United States east of the Mississippi River,
        Mississippi Valley, Illinois.
     Subjects: early exploration and settlement, trans-
        portation, Civil War, local history.
     Size: map sheets 1,100; atlases 400 vol., 400 titles.
     Serves state government agencies and public. Phst.,
        photo., commercial only.

ILLINOIS

SPRINGFIELD

152 Illinois State Library, Map Collection, Centennial Bldg.
Dorothy Bailey.
Areas: worldwide, Illinois.
Subjects: geology, transportation, military, marketing,
local history, weather, world news.
Size: map sheets 42,553; atlases 247; globe 1; relief
model 1.
Serves state officials. Restricted service on military
maps. Iln., phst., photo., micro., exch. Contains
AMS maps (30,562 sheets), U.S. Public Roads transpor-
tation maps (957 sheets), USGS topographic maps
(11,034 sheets), 37 Cook County plat books and 210
Illinois county atlases.

URBANA

153 Illinois Historical Survey, Univ. of Illinois, 416 Lincoln
Hall.
Mrs. Marguerite J. Pease, Editor.
Staff: 1; 1 p-t; specialists available: faculty.
Areas: North America, Illinois.
Subjects: history, discovery and settlement.
Size: map sheets 200 prints, 600 phst.; atlases 60 titles.
Serves faculty, graduate students and researchers.
Collection contains a small group of manuscript maps
of New Harmony and Posey County, Indiana, cataloged
and described by Arthur F. Bestor, Jr.; also the
Karpinski Collection, i.e., reproductions of maps
in the French archives; and 200 vol. of voyages,
description and travel, and gazetteers, many with
noteworthy maps.

154 Illinois State Geological Survey, Natural Resources Bldg.,
Univ. of Illinois Campus.
Vivian Gordon, Head, Mineral Resource Records Division.
Staff: 2; specialists available: geologists.
Areas: Illinois and adjacent states.
Subjects: geology.
Size: map sheets 5,000.
Serves organization and public.

ILLINOIS

URBANA

155   Univ. of Illinois, Map Library,
      Bill M. Woods, Map Librarian.
      Staff: 2; 1 p-t; specialists available: geographers,
      cartographers, translators, faculty and staff of
      Illinois State Surveys for Geology, Natural History
      and Water.
      Areas: Latin America, western and central Europe,
      Canada, United States, Illinois.
      Subjects: agriculture, city planning, marketing,
      meteorology, topography, transportation.
      Size: map sheets 150,000; atlases 3,000 vol., 2,900
      titles; globes 4; air photos 22,000.
      Serves faculty, students and public.   Iln., phst.,
      photo. (small only); micro., exch.
      Publications: New Acquisitions (bimonthly); Guide to
      the Map Collection in the University of Illinois
      (University of Illinois Library School Occasional
      Paper no. 31, December 1952); The Map Library
      (mimeo) 1953.

WHEATON

156   Wheaton College, Dept. of Social Science.
      Helen L. Smith, Associate Professor.
      Staff: 2 p-t; specialists available: geographers.
      Areas: worldwide.
      Size: map sheets 13,500; atlases 10 vol., 8 titles;
      globes 3.
      Serves faculty, students, public.   Iln., AMS depository.

INDIANA

BLOOMINGTON

157   Indiana Univ., Map Library.
      Lois Headings, Map Room Librarian.
      Staff: 1 p-t; specialists available: geographers, carto-
      graphers, translators.
      Areas: Europe, Western Europe, Indiana.
      Subjects: economic, transportation, topographic.

INDIANA

157 (continued)
    Size: map sheets 60,000-65,000; atlases 20 vol.,
        20 titles; globes 3; models 250; air photos 500.
    Serves students, faculty, public. Iln., phst.,
        photo., exch.

EAST CHICAGO

158 Inland Steel Co., Research and Development Dept.
    Virgil L. Pederson.
    Staff: 1 p-t; specialists available: translators.
    Areas: Great Lakes and St. Lawrence River, Chicago.
    Subjects: mineral resources, transportation, iron
        and steel industry.
    Size: map sheets 50; atlases 1 vol. Iln., phst.,
        photo., exch. Maps are part of the Central Infor-
        mation collection, and deal specifically with the
        research and production of the Company.

FORT WAYNE

159 Public Library of Fort Wayne and Allen County, 301 W.
    Wayne St., zone 2.
    Albert F. Diserens, Head, Reference Dept.
    Size: map sheets 500; atlases 50 vol., 50 titles;
        globes 4; air photos 12.
    Serves public.

HANOVER

160 Hanover College Library.
    Guy Campbell, Honorary Curator of the Geological Museum.
    Staff: 1 p-t.
    Areas: Indiana.
    Subjects: geology, topography, transportation.
    Size: map sheets 200; atlases 30 vol., 25 titles;
        globes 3; models 15.
    Serves faculty and students. Iln.

INDIANA

INDIANAPOLIS

161   George F. Cram Co., 730 E. Washington St., Map and Globe
      Manufacturers.
      L. B. Douthit, Vice President.
      Specialists available: geographers, cartographers,
        draftsmen, and printers.
      Areas: worldwide.
      Subjects: history.
      Size: map sheets 500; atlases 225 vol.; globes 200;
        models 30.
      Serves public. Phst., photo., actual prints, furnished
        at nominal charge; copyright permission for reproduc-
        tion available at nominal charge.
      Publications: catalogs, advertisements, reviews.

162   Indiana State Library, 140 N. Senate Ave., zone 4.
      Staff: 1 p-t.
      Areas: United States, Old Northwest Territory, Indiana.
      Subjects: geology, state and local history.
      Size: map sheets 13,799; atlases 376 vol., 254 titles.
      Serves public, state officials. Phst.

163   State Highway Commission of Indiana, State House Annex,
      zone 9.
      Tom G. Seward, State Manager, Highway Planning Survey.
        Commission does not have a map library. It does have
      a great many town, city, county and state maps which are
      part of the permanent records and files. Some of these
      were produced by the drafting dept., others gathered in
      the course of business. These various maps are of Indiana
      and cover transportation. There is also a file of air
      photos purchased from the Dept. of Agriculture. Maps
      produced by the Commission are for sale by the Indiana-
      polis Blue Print and Lithograph Co. and the H. Lieber
      Co. Maps which are part of official records are avail-
      able for inspection

INDIANA

LAFAYETTE

164 Albert A. Wells Memorial Library.
Lloyd W. Josselyn, Librarian.
Areas: worldwide.
Serves public. Depository for AMS and USGS; very few maps
are cataloged and classified.

165 Purdue Univ. Library.
George R. Meluck, Assistant Reference Librarian.
Staff: 1 p-t.
Areas: Indiana, Alaska.
Subjects: highway design.
Size: map sheets 27,000; atlases 50 (plus 227 USGS
folios), 43 titles; globes 1; models 25; air photos
750,000.
Serves faculty, students, public. Iln., phst., exch.
The models and air photos are part of the collection
of the Joint Highway Research Board.

SOUTH BEND

166 Northern Indiana Historical Society Museum, 112 South
Lafayette Blvd.
Mrs. T. E. Stanfield, Curator.
Areas: worldwide, Northwest Territory, Michigan, Ohio,
Indiana, St. Joseph County, South Bend.
Subjects: local history, forts.
Size: map sheets 150; atlases 25 vol.; models 2.
Serves public. Phst., commercial only.

IOWA

AMES

167 Iowa State College Library.
Mrs. Ruth S. Kristoffersen.
Staff: 1 p-t.
Areas: United States, Iowa.
Subjects: topography, soils, transportation.
Size: map sheets 8,000; atlases 50 vol., 35 titles.
Serves faculty and students. Phst., micro.

IOWA

AMES

168 Iowa State Highway Commission, Dept. of Safety and Traffic.
     Areas: Iowa.
     Subjects: transportation.
     Size: map sheets 300; air photos 500.
     Serves organization. Blueprints of county maps, reduced
     reprints of county maps. Maintains a complete set of
     county highway maps, brought up to date each year;
     also a collection of city and town maps, many of which
     are rather old. The county maps are available for sale
     in blue line form (1" per mile) and in printed reduc-
     tions of scales of 1/2" and 1/4" per mile. The air
     photos are from the U.S. Dept. of Agriculture.

DAVENPORT

169 Public Library, Reference Room.
     Size: map sheets 145; atlases 303 vol. (includes 218
     geologic folios).
     Serves public. Iln., phst.

HARLAN

170 R. C. Booth Enterprises.
     R. C. Booth, Owner.
     Staff: 4; 12 p-t; specialists available: geographers,
     cartographers.
     Areas: Iowa, Nebraska, South Dakota, Kansas.
     Subjects: landownership, acreages and shape of farms,
     roads, rural residents, locations on township maps,
     owners or renters, mailing addresses.
     Size: map sheets 5,600; atlases 300 vol., 300 titles.
     Serves public. Phst., offset, blueprint, blue line
     print, ozalid. Nearly complete set of Iowa Geological
     Survey available on loan. Complete lists of county
     plats and county TAM Service rural directories avail-
     able on request.

IOWA

IOWA CITY

171   State Univ. of Iowa Libraries.
Tom Garst, Assistant, Government Documents Dept. &
Map Files.
Staff: 2 p-t; specialists available: geographers,
translators.
Areas: worldwide.
Subjects: aeronautical, transportation, topographic.
Size: map sheets 35,000; atlases are part of the main
library.
Serves faculty, students, public. Iln., phst., photo.,
micro., exch. Collection is basically the AMS de-
pository set plus captured German and Japanese maps,
OSS maps (Latin America and Asia), U.S. transportation
maps, U.S. aeronautical charts, Iowa county road maps,
city plans. USGS maps are part of Geology Library.

KANSAS

LAWRENCE

172   Univ. of Kansas Libraries, Lindley Hall Branch Library.
T. R. Smith, Professor, Geography Dept.
Staff: 2 p-t.; specialists available: geographers,
cartographers, translators, staff of the Geological
Survey.
Areas: western Europe, Japan, United States, Kansas.
Subjects: geology, land use, land utilization, local
history, vegetation.
Size: map sheets 35,000 excluding duplicates; atlases
350 vol.; air photos. not est.
Serves faculty, students, State Geological Survey. Iln.,
phst., photo. (small), ozalid, drafting by special
arrangement, exch.
Publications: Typescript manual and mimeographed guide
to the collection.
In preparation by T. R. Smith: a map cataloging manual
appropriate for small libraries.

KANSAS

MANHATTAN

173 Kansas State College Library.
     Elizabeth H. Davis, Reference Librarian.
     Areas: United States.
     Subjects: geology, topography, transportation: USGS
     contour maps, folios of the Geologic Atlas of the
     United States, U.S. Public Roads Administration maps.

TOPEKA

174 Kansas State Historical Society.
     Helen M. McFarland, Librarian.
     Areas: Kansas.
     Subjects: local history.
     Size: map sheets 9,500; atlases 150 vol. (county).
     Serves public. Phst.

WICHITA

175 R. T. Aitchison, private collector, 967 Back Bay, zone 5.
     Areas: western hemisphere, Kansas.
     Subjects: Kansas boundaries.
     Size: map sheets 300; atlases 51 vol., 50 titles; Atlas
     collection runs from 1515 to date including cosmographies
     (Macrobius, Munster, Apianus, Ptolemy) atlases - Ortelius
     1584, Mercator (1636 two vol. English ed.), Blaeu (1662
     Americas), Moll, Senex, D'Anville . . .
     Maps from the 16th Century to date, mainly including the
     territory of Kansas.

176 Wichita City Library, 220 S. Main St., zone 2.
     James L. Wood, Head, Business and Technology.
     Areas: Kansas, Missouri, Iowa, Colorado, Nebraska,
     Arkansas, Texas, North and South Dakota, Oklahoma.
     Subjects: topography, geology, petroleum.
     Size: map sheets 2,100; atlases 5 vol., 5 titles.
     Serves public. Commercial photocopying.

KENTUCKY

BEREA

177   Berea College Library.
      Elizabeth Gilbert.
      Staff: 2 p-t.
      Areas: worldwide, Great Smoky Mountains in U.S.
      Subjects: geology, history, mountains.
      Size: map sheets 1,006; atlases 290 vol., 71 titles;
         globes 2; models 7.
      Serves faculty, students, public. Iln.

FRANKFORT

178   Dept. of Highways, Division of Planning.
      George D. Aaron, Manager Map Section.
      Staff: 1; specialists available: geographers,
         cartographers.
      Areas: Kentucky.
      Subjects: transportation.
      Size: map sheets 21,000; atlases 100 vol.; air photos
         14,700.
      Serves organization and public. Phst., photo., blue-
         print, lithograph.

179   Kentucky Agricultural and Industrial Development Board,
      Maps and Minerals Division, Capitol Annex. Kentucky
      Maps Collection.
      Phil M. Miles, Chief.
      Mrs. Carre Allan, Librarian.
      Staff: 1; 2 p-t; specialists available: 1 geographer,
         2 cartographers, 2 geologists, 1 engineer.
      Areas: Kentucky.
      Subjects: topography, city plans, transportation,
         geology, natural gas and electric transmission.
      Size: map sheets 1,200; air photos 20,000.
      Serves organization and public. Iln., phst., ozalid,
         black and white, exch. The Division operates a map
         library and state distribution center for topographic,
         geologic, and hydrologic data.

KENTUCKY

FRANKFORT

180 Kentucky Historical Society, Old State House.
Areas: Kentucky.
Subjects: geology, early Kentucky, early West.
Size: map sheets 1,000; atlases 20 vol.
Serves historians, geologists, genealogists. Phst.,
photo., micro., exch.

LEXINGTON

181 Univ. of Kentucky, Geology Library, Miller Hall.
Carolyn Reed, Geology Librarian.
Staff: 1; specialists available: geologists.
Areas: United States, Kentucky.
Subject: geology.
Size: map sheets 22,000.
Serves faculty, students, public. Phst. Most complete
collection of Kentucky geological maps.

182 Univ. of Kentucky, Margaret I. King Library, Archives
and Special Collections.
Staff: 1 p-t; specialists available: geographers,
translators.
Areas: Ohio River Valley, Kansas, Missouri, Kentucky.
Subjects: local history.
Size: map sheets 25,000 AMS, others not est.; atlases
120 vol., 70 titles; globes 3.
Serves university and local historians. Iln., phst.,
micro.; AMS depository cataloged.

LOUISVILLE

183 Filson Club, Inc., 118 W. Breckinridge St., zone 3.
Barbara Fitch, Acting Curator.
Areas: Ohio and Mississippi Valley, Kentucky.
Subjects: regional history.
Size: map sheets 1,710; atlases 30 vol., 30 titles.
Serves members and public. Commercial phst. and photo.
Collections has a few very old and rare maps, e.g.,
maps by Imlay, John Filson, George Rogers Clark.

KENTUCKY

LOUISVILLE

184 Louisville Free Public Library, 301-333 Library Place,
zone 3.
Edna J. Grauman, Head, Reference Dept.
Areas: United States, Kentucky, Jefferson County,
Louisville.
Subjects: topography, geology, geography, soil, sub-
surface, oil, ground water, local history.
Serves public. Phst., commercial only. Government
depository.

LOUISIANA

BATON ROUGE

185 Louisiana Dept. of Highways, General Files Unit, P.O.
Box 4245, Capitol Station, zone 4.
Homer W. Baugh, General Files Supervisor.
Staff: 5.
Areas: Louisiana.
Subjects: highways, public roads and bridges.
Serves organization and public. Phst., photo., blue
line prints.
Publications: Price List - Maps and other Engineering
Data Available for General Distribution, Jan. 1, 1953.

186 Louisiana State Univ., Dept. of Archives, Map Collection,
zone 3.
V. L. Bedsole, Dept. Head.
Marcelle F. Schertz, Reference Archivist.
Staff: 1 p-t; specialists available: faculty.
Areas: lower Mississippi Valley, Louisiana.
Subjects: local history, transportation, landownership.
Size: map sheets 1,125; manuscript vol. 22, separate
series 3.
Serves faculty, students, public. Iln., photo. (small
only), micro., exch. Most items constitute parts of
archival and manuscript collections.
Publications: Louisiana Historical Records Survey Project.
Guide to Manuscript Collections in the Department of
Archives, Louisiana State University, vol. 1. Univer-
sity, Louisiana, Dept. of Archives, 1940.

LOUISIANA

BATON ROUGE

187   Louisiana State Univ. Library, zone 3.
Areas: Louisiana.
Subjects: local history.
Size: map sheets 400; atlases 320 vol., 250 titles;
globes 1.
Serves faculty, students, public.   Iln., photo.,
ozalid, exch.   AMS depository collection in storage.
Maps and atlases are almost completely cataloged in
the classified collection or in vertical files.

188   Louisiana State Univ., School of Geology, zone 3.
Robert C. West, Assistant Professor.
Staff: 4 p-t; specialists available: geographers,
cartographers.
Subjects: topography, geology.
Size: map sheets 15,700; globes 1; models few; air
photos of Louisiana.
Serves: faculty, students.   Photo., ozalid.

NEW ORLEANS

189   Thomas F. Cunningham Reference Library, International
House, 611 Gravier St.
Areas: United States, Europe, Latin America, Africa.
Subjects: roads.
Size: map sheets 125; atlases 4 vol.
Serves public.   Iln., phst.

190   H. L. Peace Publications, 624 Gravier St., zone 12.
Ann B. Liddell, Research Dept.
Staff: p-t.
Areas: Inland waterways - Mississippi River, Intra-
coastal Waterway.
Subjects: transportation by water.
Size: river charts 11 vol.
Serves organization.   Publish trade magazines on fishing
and work boats.

LOUISIANA

NEW ORLEANS

191 Tulane Univ., Middle American Research Institute, zone 18.
       Staff: 1 p-t; specialists available: geographers, trans-
       lators, archaeologist, anthropologist.
       Areas: Mexico, Central America, West Indies.
       Subjects: archaeology, history.
       Size: map sheets 1,200; atlases 78 vol., 30 titles;
       air photos, few.
       Serves univ. and public. Commercial reproductions, exch.
       Publications: Historical Records Survey. Maps in the
       Frederick L. Hoffman Collection. 1939. (An Inventory
       of the Collections in the Middle American Research
       Institute, no. 3.) ____, Maps in the Library of the
       Middle American Research Institute. 1941. (An Inven-
       tory . . . no. 4.)

SHREVEPORT

192 Union Producing Company Library, P.O. Box 1407, zone 92.
       Jane Davies, Librarian.
       Specialists available: company engineers and special
       map makers.
       Areas: United States, Gulf South.
       Subjects: geology and topography.
       Size: map sheets 10,000 topographic quadrangles, 1,000
       geologic maps in addition to a set of USGS folios.
       Serves organization. Phst. The Mapping Dept. of the
       Company has 15,000 maps, largely private ownership
       maps for use in oil and gas production. The Geological
       Dept. has several thousand maps containing private
       geologic information. The Pipe Line Dept. has a large
       number of pipe line maps for company use. The Aerial
       Mapping Section has about 8,000 air photos.

MAINE

AUGUSTA

193 Maine State Highway Commission, Planning Survey Division,
       State House.
       Rae D. Graves, Informational Representative.
       Staff: 4; specialists available: cartographers.

MAINE

193 (continued)
Areas: Maine.
Subjects: transportation.
Size: map sheets 15,000; atlases 200.
Serves organization and public. Phst., photo.

BANGOR

194 Bangor Public Library.
Olive M. Smythe, Reference Librarian.
Staff: 1 p-t.
Areas: United States, Maine.
Subjects: topography.
Size: map sheets 22,475; atlases 185 vol., 185 titles;
globes 1.
Serves public. Iln., commercial phst.

195 Prentiss & Carlisle Co., Inc., 107 Court St.
Staff: 4 p-t; specialists available: geographers,
cartographers.
Areas: Maine.
Subjects: transportation, topography, local history.
Size: map sheets 2,000.
Serves public. Black line prints. County maps for sale.

BRUNSWICK

196 Bowdoin College Library.
J. R. McKenna, Assistant Librarian.
Staff: p-t.
Areas: worldwide.
Subjects: various.
Size: map sheets 30,000; atlases 30 vol., 30 titles.
Serves faculty, students and public.

PORTLAND

197 Maine Historical Society, 485 Congress St., zone 3.
Marian B. Rowe, Librarian.
Areas: New England, Maine.
Subjects: local history, transportation, topography.
Serves organization, public. Iln., phst. and photo.,
commercial.

MAINE

197   (continued)
      Publications: Smith, Edgar Crosby. Maps of the State of
      Maine; A Bibliography of the Maps of the State of
      Maine. Privately printed, 1903.
      A Reference List of Manuscripts Relating to the History
      of Maine. 1938.

198   Portland Public Library, 619 Congress St., zone 3.
      Dorothy Packard, Assistant Reference Librarian.
      Staff: 1 p-t.
      Area: Maine
      Subjects: local history.
      Size: map sheets 3,410; atlases 59 vol., 57 titles;
      globes 1.
      Serves public. Phst., commercial.

WATERVILLE

199   Colby College Library.
      Staff: p-t.
      Areas: worldwide, United States.
      Subjects: topography, geology, local history.
      Size: map sheets 60,000; atlases 25 vol., 20 titles;
      globes 1; air photos 500.
      Serves faculty, students and public. AMS and USGS
      depository.

MARYLAND

ANNAPOLIS

200   Maryland State Library.
      Areas: Maryland, state and counties, adjoining states.
      Size: map sheets 50.
      Serves public. Phst. available through Maryland Hall
      of Records.

MARYLAND

BALTIMORE

201   Edward S. Corcoran, private collector, 908 St. Paul St.,
      zone 2.
      Areas: America.
      Subjects: history, early Americana.
      Size: map sheets 40; atlases 100 vol., 100 titles.
      Iln., limited, but available to scholars.

202   Dept. of Public Works, Bureau of Surveys, Baltimore
      Municipal Office Bldg., zone 2.
      Edward J. Hecker.
      Specialists available: engineers, draftsmen.
      Areas: Baltimore and environs.
      Serves organization and public. Phst.; published maps
      for sale.

203   Enoch Pratt Free Library, General Reference Dept., Map
      Collection, 400 Cathedral St., zone 1.
      Margaret Sheffey.
      Staff: 2 p-t.
      Areas: worldwide.
      Subjects: various.
      Size: map sheets 36,000; atlases over 300 vol.;
          globes 6.
      Serves public. Iln., phst., other photoduplication.
      Publications: General Reference Dept. Staff Manual.
          Baltimore, Enoch Pratt Free Library, 1950, p. 195-222.

204   Enoch Pratt Free Library, Maryland Dept.
      Elizabeth Litsinger, Librarian.
      Areas: Maryland, Baltimore.
      Size: map sheets 1,360; atlases 20 vol.

205   Johns Hopkins Univ. Library, Geography Library, zone 18.
      Mrs. J. K. Brigstocke, Geography Librarian.
      Staff: 1 p-t; specialists available: geographers,
          cartographers, translators.
      Areas: worldwide.
      Subjects: fairly well-rounded, specializing in geology.
      Size: map sheets 35,000; atlases 150 vol.
      Serves faculty, students, staff. Iln., phst., photo.
          small only.

MARYLAND

06 Johns Hopkins Univ., John Work Garrett Library, Evergreen
House, 4545 N. Charles St., zone 10.
   Elizabeth Baer, Librarian.
   Staff: 1.
   Areas: America, Maryland before 1800.
   Subjects: American colonial period, local history,
      railroads and canals of early 19th Century; general
      atlases of 17th-18th Centuries.
   Size: map sheets 50 before 1800; atlases 30 vol., 25
      titles; 100 rare books.
   Serves faculty and students. Phst., photo. This ia a
      rare book collection left to the university.
   Publications: Baer, E. Seventeenth Century Maryland;
      A Bibliography. Baltimore, 1949. Contains description
      of Maryland maps of 17th Century.

07 Maryland Bureau of Control Surveys and Maps, 307 Tower
Bldg., zone 2.
   George W. Cassell, Engineer-in-Charge.
   Staff: 4 full time, about 25 percent of their time is
      consumed on maps.
   Areas: Maryland, Washington, D.C.
   Subjects: transportation, road types, traffic volume,
      geology, and town boundaries.
   Size: map sheets 2,000; models 6; air photos 250.
   Serves Maryland State Roads Commission, surveyors,
      engineers, public. lln., blueprints, exch.

08 Maryland Historical Society, 201 W. Monument St., zone 1.
   Fred Shelley, Librarian.
   Staff: 1 p-t.
   Areas: Maryland.
   Subjects: history.
   Size: map sheets 175; atlases 25 vol.
   Serves the Society and public. Phst., photo.

09 Peabody Institute Library, 1 E. Mt. Vernon Place, zone 2.
   Lloyd A. Brown, Librarian.
   Specialists available: cartographer, cartographic historian.
   Areas: western Europe, United States, Maryland, Baltimore.
   Subjects: local history, maps of early Maryland and
      Baltimore, atlases of the sixteenth to the ninteenth
      centuries.

MARYLAND

209   (continued)
Size: map sheets 2,500; atlases 325 vol., 250 titles.
Serves public. Iln., phst. Many maps not analyzed
in an extensive collection of voyages and travels.

BELTSVILLE

210   U.S. Soil Conservation Service, Agricultural Research
Center, Division of Cartography, Map Files.
Katherine M. Laupp.
Staff: 1; 1 p-t; specialists available: cartographers.
Areas: United States, Alaska, Hawaii, Puerto Rico.
Subjects: topography.
Serves organization and public. Phst., photo., ozalid,
offset lithography.

COLLEGE PARK

211   Univ. of Maryland Library.
Mrs. Harold Hayes, Map Librarian.
Staff: p-t; specialists available: faculty in the
Geography and Foreign Language Depts.
Areas: Maryland
Subjects: local history.
Size: map sheets 10,000; atlases 45 vol.; globes 1;
air photos on versos of Army maps.
Serves faculty, students, public. Exch. A city map
collection is being developed in connection with a
telephone directory and annual city report service.

FROSTBURG

212   State Teachers College.
Helen Y. Hough.
Staff: 1 p-t; specialists available: geographers.
Areas: Maryland.
Size: map sheets 679; atlases 12 vol., 12 titles;
globes 3; models 2; air photos 19.
Serves faculty, students, public. Iln., exch.

MASSACHUSETTS

AMHERST

213 Amherst College Library.
Newton F. McKeon, Director.
Areas: worldwide.
Collection has set of sheets and atlases of the USGS and
representative atlases for general reference use.
Serves organization. AMS depository.

ANDOVER

214 Philips Academy, Robert S. Peabody Foundation for Archaeology.
Areas: 7-1/2 minute series Massachusetts and Rhode Island;
15 minute series for Connecticut. All available sheets
of the 15 minute series of New Hampshire and Maine; all
available topographic survey maps of eastern Canada.
Serves organization.

BOSTON

215 Boston Athenaeum Library, 10-1/2 Beacon St., zone 8.
Areas: worldwide, New England.
Subjects: various.
Size: map sheets 4,000; atlases 600 vol., 500 titles;
globes 3.
Serves organization and visiting scholars. Phst., micro.

216 Boston Public Library, Maps Dept. (projected), Copley Square,
zone 17.
(Chief of dept. to be appointed.)
Richard G. Hensley, Chief Librarian, Division of Reference
and Research Services.
Specialists available: geographers, translators.
Areas: worldwide, Western Hemisphere, New England,
Massachusetts, Boston.
Subjects: local history, early navigation atlases;
Ptolemaic atlases.
Size: map sheets 37,000; atlases 2,100 vol., 2,100
titles; globes 1.
Serves public. Phst., photo.; a Maps Dept. is to be
established probably in the latter part of 1953 which
will bring together the collection of maps in the
Library. AMS depository.

MASSACHUSETTS

BOSTON

217   Boston Univ. Chenery Library, 725 Commonwealth Ave., zone 15.
     Size: map sheets 1,100; atlases 40 vol.,   25 titles;
       globes 1; USGS folios 175.
     Serves faculty and students.   Iln., commercial reproduc-
       tions only; map collection is partly in Reference
       Room, partly in subject depts.

218   The Bostonian Society, Old State House, zone 9.
     Areas: Boston and environs.
     Subjects: local history.
     Size: map sheets 250; atlases 1 vol., 1 title; air
       photos 20.
     Serves researchers. Iln.

219   Ernest Dudley Chase, 1000 Washington St., zone 18.
     Pictorial maps.

220   Christian Science Monitor Library,   1 Norway St., zone 15.
     Joan Nilson, Assistant in Charge of Maps.
     Staff: 1 p-t; specialists available: geographers,
       cartographers, translators.
     Areas: worldwide, with emphasis on foreign.
     Subjects: various.
     Size: map sheets 18,000; atlases 40 vol., 40 titles.
     Serves organization. Phst. for material published in
       The Christian Science Monitor.

221   Harvard Business School, Baker Library, Soldiers Field,
     zone 63.
     Robert W. Lovett, Head of the Manuscript Division.
     Staff: 1 p-t; specialists available: translators.
     Areas: worldwide, United States, New England.
     Subjects: business, transportation, communication,
       public utilities, market analysis.
     Size: map sheets 792; atlases 16 vol., 10 titles;
       globes 1.
     Serves faculty, students and public.   Iln., phst.,
       photo, micro., exch.

MASSACHUSETTS

BOSTON

222 Insurance Library Association of Boston, Sanborn Map Collection, 89 Broad St., zone 10.
     Abbie G. Glover, Librarian.
     Areas: New England, except Boston.
     Subjects: building construction, water supply, occupancy
        hazards; all for insurance purposes.
     Size: atlases 600 vol.
     Serves organization.

223 Massachusetts Historical Society, 1154 Boylston St., zone 15.
     Stephen T. Riley, Librarian.
     Size: map sheets 500; atlases 200.

224 State Library of Massachusetts, 341 State House, zone 33.
     Miss E.B. Lewis, Reference Assistant.
     Staff: 1 p-t.
     Areas: worldwide, Massachusetts.
     Subjects: local history, railroads, topography.
     Size: map sheets 14,326; atlases 454 vol.
     Serves public and state officials. Phst. Maps fully
        cataloged.
     Publications: Maps and Plans Section in Catalogue of
        the State Library of Massachusetts. 1880, p. 1031-1047.

BROOKLINE

225 Zion Research Library, 120 Seaver St., zone 46.
     Staff: p-t.
     Areas: Bible lands.
     Subjects: Bible history.
     Size: map sheets 250; atlases 12 vol., 12 titles;
        models 1.
     Serves public, Bible students. Iln.

MASSACHUSETTS

CAMBRIDGE

226 Harvard College Library, Winsor Memorial Map Room, Widener
     Library (including the collection in the Institute of Geo-
     graphical Exploration, now closed).
     Robert H. Haynes, Assistant Librarian.
     Mrs. Kirk Bryan, Assistant in Charge of Maps.
     Staff: 1.
     Areas: Europe, USSR, United States, especially early
        maps, Canada.
     Subjects: 16th & 17th Century maps and atlases, early
        American maps, topographic maps, Massachusetts aerial
        photos.
     Size: map sheets 150,000; atlases 1,700 vol., 1,500
        titles; globes 7 (including 2 Mercator, 2 Bonaldi);
        models 25; air photos 250; wall maps 800.
     Serves public. Iln., phst., photo, micro., exch.
     Publications: Harvard University Map Catalogue.
        Cambridge, E.W. Metcalf & Co. 1831. Library
        of Harvard University - Descriptive and Historical
        Notes. Fourth Edition, p. 110.

227 Erwin Raisz, private collector, 107 Washington Ave.,
     zone 40.
     Specialists available: geographers, cartographers,
        translators.
     Areas: worldwide.
     Subjects: small scale maps.
     Size: map sheets 7,000, about 3,000 of these are samples
        of the cartographic work of Raisz; atlases 120 vols.;
        globes 5; models 5; air photos 300.
     Serves owner. Iln., exch.; about 10,000 maps in stock
        for sale.

228 Massachusetts Institute of Technology, Boston Stein Club
     Map Room, also Theodore Schwarz Map Collection, Charles
     Hayden Memorial Library.
     Eleanor L. Bartlett, Special Collections Librarian.
     Staff: 1 p-t.
     Areas: worldwide.
     Subjects: various.

MASSACHUSETTS

228 (continued)
    Size: map sheets 30,000; atlases 200 vol., globes 25;
    models, few; air photos, few.
    Serves faculty, students, occasionally others. Phst.,
    photo., micro.

FRAMINGHAM

229 State Teachers College Library.
    Specialists available: geographer.
    Size: map sheets 300; atlases 33; globes 4; relief
    models 7; wall maps 100.
    Serves organization. Iln., exch.

LOWELL

230 Lowell City Library.
    Areas: Massachusetts, Middlesex County, Suffolk County,
    Lowell, Boston.
    Subjects: local history.
    Size: map sheets 350; atlases 3.
    Serves public.

NEWTON

231 Newton Public Library, 414 Centre St.
    Harold A. Wooster, Librarian.
    Subjects: local history.
    Size: map sheets 200; atlases 75 titles.
    Serves public.

232 The University Prints, private collection of Robert E.
    LaMont, P.O. Box 5, zone 58.
    Size: atlases 30-35 vol.; globes 1; models 2.
    Collection contains source material for making "art
    maps" and plans of ancient cities, which are sold
    commercially.

MASSACHUSETTS

NORTHAMPTON

233   Forbes Library, West St.
       Honora Flahive, Reference Librarian.
       Areas: Hampshire County and Northampton.
       Subjects: local history.
       Size: map sheets 6,458; atlases 407 vol., 406 titles;
          globes 1; air photos 2.
       Serves public. Iln.

SALEM

234   Essex Institute, 132-134 Essex St.
       Staff: 3 p-t.
       Areas: New England.
       Subjects: local history, marine, geology.
       Serves public. Phst., photo. Collection includes
          New England Coast Pilots.

WATERTOWN

235   Perkins Institution Library, zone 72.
       Nelson Coon, Librarian.
       Subjects: embossed maps for use of the blind. Covers
          period from about 1800 to 1950.
       Size: models 100.
       Serves organization; Collection includes maps made for
          use in the schools of Germany, France, England and
          United States.

WELLESLEY

236   Wellesley College, Dept. of Geology and Geography, zone 18.
       Margaret M. Steele, Secretary and Custodian.
       Staff: 1 p-t; specialists available: geographers, carto-
          graphers, geologists.
       Areas: worldwide.
       Subjects: geology.
       Size: map sheets 100,000; atlases 100 vol.; globes 5;
          models 100; air photos 600.
       Serves faculty, students and public. Depository for
          AMS and USGS.

MASSACHUSETTS

WILLIAMSTOWN

237 Williams College Library.
     Areas: worldwide.
     Subjects: geology, history.
     Size: map sheets 12,000; atlases 100; globes 1;
        models 1; air photos 6.
     Serves organization and public. Iln.

WORCESTER

238 American Antiquarian Society, Park Ave. and Salisbury
     St., zone 9.
        C. K. Shipton, Librarian.
        Staff: 1 p-t.
        Areas: United States.
        Subjects: various.
        Size: map sheets 9,800; atlases 560 vol.; globes 2.
        Serves public. Photo.

239 Clark Univ. Library Map Collection, 1 Downing St., zone 10.
        Guy H. Burnham, Map Librarian.
        Staff: 1 p-t; specialists available: geographers, carto-
           graphers, translators.
        Areas: worldwide.
        Subjects: physical, political, economic.
        Size: map sheets 50,000; atlases 300 titles; globes 5;
           models 20; air photos 1,200 of Massachusetts.
        Serves univ. and public. Iln., exch.

MICHIGAN

ANN ARBOR

240 Univ. of Michigan, The Clements Library.
        Christian Brun, Assistant Curator.
        Staff: 1 p-t; specialists available: geographers, carto-
           graphers, translators, Univ. faculty, Michigan Histor-
           ical Collection staff.
        Areas: North America, United States, Michigan.
        Subjects: historical cartography, exploration, French
           and Indian War, American Revolution.

240   (continued)
Size: map sheets 28,000; atlases 516 vol., 436 titles;
globes 5.
Serves faculty, advanced students, public. Phst., photo,
micro.
Publications: Adams, Randolph.   British Headquarters
Maps and Sketches . . . Ann Arbor, 1928; Peckham,
Howard H.   Guide to the Manuscript Collections in
the William L. Clements Library.   Ann Arbor, 1942;
A guide is now being prepared which will describe
the Library's manuscript maps.

241   Univ. of Michigan, Map Library.
Staff: 1 p-t; specialists available: geographers,
translators.
Areas: worldwide, Michigan.
Subjects: local history, geology, topography, city plans.
Size: map sheets 62,000; atlases 400 vol., 250 titles.
Serves faculty and students.   Iln., phst., micro.

242   Univ. of Michigan, Michigan Historical Collections, 160
Rackham Bldg.
Ida C. Brown, Assistant Curator.
Staff: 1 p-t.
Areas: Michigan.
Size: map sheets 900; atlases 65 vol.
Serves faculty, students, public.   Iln. atlases only,
phst., photo., exch.

BLOOMFIELD HILLS

243   Cranbrook Institute of Science.
Virginia K. Tiede, Librarian.
Areas: United States, Michigan.
Subjects: geology, topography.
Size: map sheets 710; atlases 6 vol., 6 titles; globes
1; models 1.
Serves members and staff.   Maps are part of the library
of natural science publications.

MICHIGAN

DETROIT

244 Brooke, Smith, French and Dorrance, Inc., 8469 E.
Jefferson, zone 14.
Joan O'Flanagan, Librarian.
Staff: 1 p-t.
Areas: United States.
Subjects: marketing.
Size: map sheets 100; atlases 6 vol., 6 titles.
Serves organization.

245 Detroit Metropolitan Area Regional Planning Commission,
1002 Cadillac Square Bldg., zone 26.
Wesley F. Furton.
Staff: 2 p-t; specialists available: geographer,
cartographer, junior planners.
Areas: Detroit metropolitan.
Subjects: regional planning, land use, water, sewer,
transportation, recreation, population, business,
industry.
Size: map sheets 800; air photos 20.
Serves public. Phst., photo, ozalid, litho-offset
prints.
Publications: Catalog of maps and charts available
as of Jan. 1, 1951 (mimeo.)

246 Detroit Public Library, Burton Historical Collection,
5201 Woodward, zone 2.
Mrs. Elleine Stones, Chief.
Staff: p-t.
Areas: Michigan, Old Northwest, St. Lawrence River,
early United States, Canada.
Subjects: local history.
Size: map sheets 3,334; atlases 500 vol., 500 titles;
air photos of Detroit.
Serves public. Iln., phst., commercial photo. and
micro.

MICHIGAN

DETROIT

247 Detroit Public Library, History and Travel Dept., 5201
     Woodward, zone 2.
         Rae Elizabeth Rips, Chief.
         Staff: 1; 6 p-t.
         Areas: worldwide, Canada, Michigan, Detroit.
         Subjects: topography, roads.
         Size: map sheets 59,000; atlases 550 vol., 525 titles;
             globes 4; models 3.
         Serves public. Iln., phst., commercial photo. Collec-
             tion cataloged. Books analyzed for maps.

248 Otto O. Fisher, private collector, 2475 Iroquois Ave.,
     zone 14.
         Specialists available: geographers, cartographers,
             translators.
         Areas: America, Northwest Territory.
         Subjects: history, art, travel.
         Size: map sheets 100; atlases 136 vol., 110 titles;
             globes 3 plus books about globes; air photos 2;
             manuscript and fore edge maps, not est.
         Serves educational institutions and libraries, especially
             in the Detroit area. Iln., exhibits have been loaned
             to all parts of the United States. Phst., photo., exch.,
             Collection includes Bleau, Ptolemy, and Mercator atlases.

249 Hearne Brothers, map publishers, 25th Floor, National Bank
     Bldg.
         Staff: 103; specialists available: geographers and carto-
             graphers at commercial rates.
         Areas: worldwide, particularly continents and cities.
         Subjects: various.
         Size: map sheets 200,000.
         Serves schools and businesses.
         Publications: Commercial and School Map Catalogs.

250 U.S. Lake Survey, Corps. of Engineers, U.S. Army, Room 630,
     Federal Bldg., zone 26.
         C. D. Tyndall and Elmer F. Kulp, Jr.
         Specialists available: cartographers, hydrographers and
             geodesists.

MICHIGAN

250 (continued)
Areas: charts of the Great Lakes and connecting waters,
Lake Champlain, Minnesota-Ontario Border Lakes and New
York State canals; basic survey drawings.
Subjects: hydrographic navigation charts.
Size: map sheets 2,100.
Serves Great Lakes navigators and Government agencies.
Lithograph. Publishes hydrographic navigation charts
which are sold to commercial and private nagivators.
The only charts available are those listed in the
Catalog . . . and copies of basic survey drawings
sold at cost of reproduction.
Publication: U.S. Lake Survey, Survey of the Northern,
and Northwestern Lakes. Catalog of Charts of the
Great Lakes and Connecting Waters, Lake Champlain,
New York Canals, Minnesota-Ontario Border Lakes.
Edition of 1953. 16 p.

EAST LANSING

251 Michigan State College Library.
Richard Leach.
Staff: 1 p-t.
Areas: worldwide, United States.
Subjects: geology, transportation, soils, city plans.
Size: map sheets 34,794.
Serves faculty and students. Iln., phst.

FLINT

252 The Flint Journal, Editorial Library, zone 2.
William D. Chase, Librarian (and professional geographer).
Staff: 2; 2 p-t.
Areas: Michigan, Genesee County, Flint.
Subjects: local history, roads.
Size: map sheets 150; atlases 12 vol., 10 titles;
globes 1; air photos 75.
Serves organization. Autostat, photo, exch. A newspaper
reference library which contains clipping files, books,
and pamphlets.

MICHIGAN

HOUGHTON

253 Michigan College of Mining and Technology.
Staff: 1 p-t; specialists available: geologists,
geographers, translators.
Areas: Canada, United States.
Subjects: geology, transportation.
Serves faculty and students, occasionally local mining
industry. Iln., phst., photo., exch., AMS depository.

KALAMAZOO

254 Western Michigan College.
Size: map sheets 15,000.
Serves faculty, students. AMS depository.

LANSING

255 Michigan Historical Commission, Lewis Cass Bldg.
Areas: Michigan.
Subjects: history.
Size: map sheets 540; atlases 6 vol., 6 titles.
Serves organization and public. Phst., photo.
Publications: Karpinski, Louis C. Bibliography of
the Printed Maps of Michigan, 1804-1880 . . .
Lansing, Michigan Historical Commission, 1931.

256 Michigan State Library, 125 E. Shiawassee St.
Mrs. Loleta D. Fyan, State Librarian.
Gail Curtis, Reference Section.
Areas: Michigan.
Subjects: geology; local history.
Size: map sheets 7,179; atlases 153 titles.
Serves state departments and public. Iln., phst.,
exch.

PORT HURON

257 Port Huron Public Library, William Lee Jenks Collection.
Leila B. Wilcox, Librarian.
Areas: Great Lakes, Michigan.
Subjects: local history.
Size: map sheets 2,000.
Serves public. Phst., photo., exch.

MINNESOTA

MINNEAPOLIS

258   Hennepin County Historical Society, 1516 Harmon Pl., zone 3.
      Joseph W. Zalusky, Director of Museum and Executive
        Secretary.
      Areas: Hennepin County.
      Subjects: local history, geology.
      Size: small.

259   Minneapolis Public Library.
      Specialists available: Univ. of Minnesota staff.
      Areas: United States, Minnesota and surrounding states.
      Subjects: topography, local history.
      Size: map sheets 15,350; atlases 700 vol., 500 titles;
        globes 1.
      Serves public. Iln., phst., maps are in Reference, Clip-
        ping, and Circulation collections and at branches; no
        separate map collection.

260   Minneapolis Public Library, Business and Municipal Branch,
      217 S. Sixth St., zone 2.
      Maud Briggs, Branch Librarian.
      Areas: Minnesota.
      Subjects: land plats of local and surrounding areas.
      Size: map sheets 1,000; atlases 30 vol., 30 titles.
      Serves public.

261   Univ. of Minnesota Library, zone 14.
      Elizabeth B. Henderson, Senior Librarian.
        Staff: 2 p-t; specialists available: geographers, carto-
          graphers, translators, Minnesota Geological Survey,
          faculty.
      Areas: Canada, Minnesota.
      Subjects: topography, local history.
      Size: map sheets 40,000; air photos 25,765.
      Serves faculty, students, public. Phst., photo., micro.
        All atlases are shelved in the stacks with other geo-
        graphical material. The map collection is cataloged
        under area and author, and two sets of cards maintained,
        one for the Map Room and one for the Reference Dept.

MINNESOTA

NORTHFIELD

262 Carleton College.
      Duncan Stewart, Jr.
      Staff: 1 p-t.
      Areas: worldwide.
      Subjects: transportation, topography, captured German,
        Italian and Japanese maps.
      Size: map sheets 71,000; atlases 10 vol.; globes 1;
        relief models 1; air photos 750.
      Serves organization, public. Iln.

    ST. PAUL

263 Ames Library of South Asia, Inc., 50 W. Kellogg Blvd., zone 2.
      Lois Cuhel, Assistant.
      Staff: 1 p-t.
      Areas: South Asia, i.e., India, Pakistan, Burma, Ceylon,
        Afghanistan and Nepal.
      Subjects: history.
      Size: map sheets 600; atlases 257 vol., 31 titles.
      Serves graduate students and others interested in Indian
        history.

264 James Jerome Hill Reference Library.
      Size: not est.
      Serves public. Collection contains general reference
        atlases, topographic maps, geologic publications, 175
        maps published by the British War Office between 1901
        and 1921, and a few of the sets issued by such Federal
        agencies as the General Land Office, the Mississippi
        River Commission and the International Boundary Com-
        mission.

265 Minnesota Dept. of Education, Library Division, 369 State
      Office Bldg., zone 1.
      Russell J. Schunk, State Director of Libraries.
      Areas: Minnesota.
      Size: map sheets 150; atlases 10 vol., 10 titles.
      Serves public. Iln.

MINNESOTA

ST. PAUL

266 St. Paul Public Library, zone 2.
Ralph Huebscher, Reference Librarian.
Mabel McCoy, Reference Librarian.
Staff: 2 p-t.
Areas: worldwide.
Subjects: topographic maps of U.S. to 1946.
Size: map sheets 15,210; atlases 150 vol., 138 titles;
globes 4; air photos 50 - 100.
Serves public. Iln., AMS depository.

MISSISSIPPI

JACKSON

267 Dept. of Archives and History.
William D. McCain, Director.
Mrs. Adlai Morgan.
Staff: p-t.
Areas: Mississippi.
Size: map sheets 500.
Serves public. Phst.

268 Mississippi State Highway Dept., Traffic and Planning Division, 412 Woodrow Wilson Drive.
Carl Vernon Corley, Chief Draftsman.
Staff: 5; 2 p-t.
Areas: Mississippi.
Subjects: transportation, geology.
Serves organization and public. Iln., blue line prints
made from film and paper negatives. Although there are
on hand various maps and atlases of county and state to
be issued out or sold, the collection consists mainly
of negatives from which prints are made upon request.

STATE COLLEGE

269 Mississippi State College Library.
Miss Sidney Gay, Assistant Reference Librarian in charge
of Government Documents.
Staff: 1 p-t; specialists available: geographers.

MISSISSIPPI

269 (continued)
Areas: United States, Mississippi.
Subjects: geology, topography.
Size: map sheets 8,504; atlases 45 vol.; globes 2; air
photos 58.
Serves faculty, students, public. Iln., phst., micro.
Attempt to keep a complete set of USGS topographic
quadrangles for United States.

VICKSBURG

270 Mississippi River Commission, Corps. of Engineers, U.S.
Army, P.O. Box 80.
D.H. Grolock, Chief, Service Section, Engineering Division.
Staff: 1; 2 p-t; specialists available: geographers,
cartographers, translators.
Areas: Alluvial Valley, Lower Mississippi River, and Mississippi River and tributaries below Cairo, Illinois to
Gulf of Mexico; also States of Illinois, Missouri, Arkansas, Kentucky, Tennessee, Mississippi, and Louisiana,
within above region.
Subjects: flood control, navigation, rivers and harbors,
topography, hydrography, hydrometry, geology, and related subjects.
Size: map sheets 1,000; atlases 100 vol.; air photos and
pamphlets not est. In addition the Map Files include
some 25,000 sheets of surveys, cross sections, plans,
hydrographs, and related data.
Serves organization and public. Iln., phst., photo.,
ozalid, blueprint, exch. The maps and publications of
the Commission are on file in the larger public libraries,
educational and scientific institutions in the United
States and some European countries.
Publications: topographic quadrangles, maps, charts, index
maps, lists of publications and maps available.

MISSOURI

CAPE GIRARDEAU

271 State College, Kent Library.
F.E. Snider, Librarian.

MISSOURI

71 (continued)
   Staff: p-t; specialists available: professors of geography
      and geology.
   Areas: Missouri.
   Size: map sheets 500; atlases 50 vol., 45 titles; globes 1.
   Serves faculty and students. Iln., phst. (legal size
      maximum).

COLUMBIA

72 Univ. of Missouri, General Library, Map Dept.
   Mrs. Jane Cave, Map Librarian.
   Staff: 1; 1 p-t; specialists available: geographers,
      translators, faculty.
   Areas: United States, Missouri.
   Subjects: topography, geology.
   Size: map sheets 50,000; atlases 150 titles; globes 1;
      air photos 167.
   Serves faculty, students, public. Iln. for maps only; phst.,
      photo., micro., exch. Since the Map Dept. as such was
      organized only a few years ago it has not yet developed
      any specializations in area or subject. The Library as
      a depository has received USGS and other maps for much
      longer, however. There are about 17,300 cataloged sheets
      in the General Library; this includes only copy one of
      AMS depository maps. The rest are in branch libraries
      and have not been cataloged. They consist mainly of
      topographic and geologic quadrangles.

JEFFERSON CITY

273 Missouri State Highway Dept.
   Rex M. Whitton, Chief Engineer.
   Staff (map making): 10.
   Areas: Missouri.
   Subjects: highways.
   Size: map sheets for 114 counties.
   Serves organization and public. Phst., photo.

MISSOURI

JEFFERSON CITY

274 Missouri State Library, State Office Bldg.
     Polley Bignell, Reference Librarian.
     Staff: 4 p-t.
     Areas: United States.
     Size: map sheets 125; atlases 35 vol., 35 titles.
     Serves public. Iln., portable copyfix.

KANSAS CITY

275 Kansas City Art Institute and School of Design, 4415
     Warwick Blvd.
     Mary Roberts Couchman, Librarian.
     Staff: 1 p-t.
     Areas: worldwide.
     Subjects: various.
     Size: map sheets 300; atlases 3 vol.
     Serves students. Iln., phst.

276 Kansas City Public Library, 9th and Locust Sts.
     Idris Smith, Head, Business and Technical Dept.
     Staff: p-t.
     Areas: Missouri Valley.
     Subjects: topographic, army, and soil.
     Size: map sheets 30,000.
     Serves public. Commercial phst.

ROLLA

277 Univ. of Missouri, School of Mines and Metallurgy.
     O.R. Grawe, Chairman, Geology Dept.
     Staff: 1 p-t; specialists available: geologists.
     Areas: United States, Missouri.
     Subjects: geology, topography.
     Size: map sheets 6,000; air photos 4,000.
     Serves faculty, students, public. Collection comprises
       all topographic and geologic maps issued by USGS plus
       some maps depicting foreign geology. Aerial-photo
       coverage for about 100 quadrangles in United States.

MISSOURI

ST. LOUIS

278 Harold A. Bulger, M.D., private collector, 4405 W. Pine
Blvd., zone 8.
   Areas: western United States, Mississippi Valley,
      St. Louis.
   Subjects: exploration, history, transportation.
   Size: map sheets 1,930.

279 Missouri Historical Society, Jefferson Memorial Bldg., zone 12.
   Barbara Kell, Reference Librarian.
   Staff: 1 p-t.
   Areas: Louisiana Purchase, Missouri, St. Louis.
   Size: map sheets 585; atlases 125 vol., 114 titles.
   Serves members, students, historians. Iln., phst.,
      photo.; exch.

280 Eric P. Newman, private collector, 6450 Cecil Ave., zone 5.
   Areas: Mississippi Valley, prior to 1850.
   Size: map sheets 25; atlases 50 vol. Iln. Collection
      is a hobby.

281 St. Louis Public Library, 1301 Olive St.
   Mildred Boatman, Chief, Reference Dept.
   Mrs. Marie Roberts, Assistant, Reference Dept.
   Staff: 2 p-t.
   Areas: worldwide.
   Subjects: local history.
   Size: map sheets 32,236; atlases 333 vol., 284 titles;
      globes 2.
   Serves public. Iln., phst.
   Publications: Boatman, Mildred. Maps in the St. Louis
      Public Library. St. Louis, 1931.

282 St. Louis Univ. Libraries, Technology Library, 3621 Olive
   St., zone 8.
   Elsie Kling, Librarian.
   Staff: 2 p-t; specialists available: geographers, faculty.
   Areas: United States.
   Subjects: geology, geophysical investigations, topography.
   Size: map sheets 9,650; atlases 389 vol., 4 titles.
   Serves faculty, students. Exch.

MISSOURI

ST. LOUIS

283 Union Electric Co. of Missouri, 315 North 12th St., zone 1.
     Areas: Missouri, Illinois, Iowa.
     Subjects: topography, city plans.
     Size: map sheets 150; atlases 8 vol.
     Serves organization. Phst., photo.

284 USAF Aeronautical Chart and Information Center, Library,
     Map/Chart Branch and Aeronautical Charts Depository, 2nd
     and Arsenal Sts., zone 18.
     Charles J. Guenther, Accountable Library Officer.
     Staff: 9; specialists available: geographers, carto-
        graphers, translators, photogrammetrists.
     Areas: worldwide.
     Subjects: air navigation.
     Size: map sheets 395,000 (including 119,000 USAF charts);
        technical publications 1,200 vol., 1,000 titles; globes
        1; models 1; air photos, few.
     Serves organization; provides maps and charts to authorized
        federal agencies and to USAF chart contractors. Iln.,
        phst., photo., exch. - security clearance must be obtained
        by borrowing agency or contractor before classified mate-
        rials may be exchanged in accordance with existing regu-
        lations. Entire collection is cataloged; maps and charts
        by area and producer. No printed cards used.
     Publications: USAF ACIC Regulation 212-1, Library Policy,
        Activities and Procedures. USAF ACIC Publication RM-71
        (published release giving facts on background of aero-
        nautical charts and history of USAF Aeronautical Chart
        and Information Center).

285 Washington Univ., Geology Library, zone 5.
     Mrs. Harriet K. Long, Librarian.
     Staff: 1 p-t; specialists available: geographers.
     Areas: United States.
     Subjects: geology, oil and gas, topography.
     Size: map sheets 70,000; atlases 35 vol., 35 titles;
        globes 1.
     Serves faculty and students. Depository for AMS and USGS.

MONTANA

BILLINGS

286 Parmly Billings Memorial Library.
Ann Whitmack, Librarian.
Staff: 1 p-t.
Areas: Montana.
Subjects: history, geology.
Size: map sheets 100; atlases 10 vol.
Serves public. Commercial reproduction. Rare maps of
historical interest to the region are in many cases
framed and glass covered but may be photographed.

BOZEMAN

287 Montana State College Library.
Areas: United States, Missouri River basin, Montana.
Subjects: geology, oil, coal, local history.
Size: map sheets 7,500; atlases 20 vol.
Serves faculty and students. Phst.; USGS quadrangles of
the 48 states.

HELENA

288 Historical Society of Montana, Maps of Montana.
Rita McDonald, Librarian.
Areas: western Canada, northwest United States, Montana.
Subjects: geology, local history, transportation, others.
Serves public.

289 Montana Highway Commission, Planning Survey.
Carl A. Wirth, Mapping Supervisor.
Staff: 3 in map drafting.
Areas: Montana.
Subjects: planimetric maps of counties.
Size: map sheets 285.
Serves organization and public. Black and white contact
printing. Not a collection or library of maps but a
file of county maps prepared by the survey for the use
of the Highway Dept. and other state and federal
agencies.

NEBRASKA

LINCOLN

290   Nebraska Dept. of Roads and Irrigation, State House, zone 9.
      C.G. McGraw, Manager, Equipment and Supplies.
      Specialists available: engineering staff.
      Areas: Nebraska.
      Subjects: transportation, traffic flow.
      Size: map sheets 1,000; air photos 19,850.
      Serves organization and public. Blueprints, blue line,
        black and white prints, multilith, phst. (small),
        photo. (small). The Dept. makes maps which are avail-
        able to the public at a nominal price. The Dept. does
        not have a map library, but rather a file of A.A.A. air
        photos, covering the state, scale 1:20,000; USGS maps;
        county soil maps.

291   Nebraska State Historical Society, 1500 R St.
      John B. White, Librarian.
      Staff: 1 p-t; faculty of the Univ. of Nebraska may be
        consulted.
      Areas: plains of the United States, Nebraska.
      Subjects: local history.
      Size: map sheets 3,000; atlases 230 vol., 220 titles.
      Serves organization and public. Iln., commercial phst.,
        Conturas for small parts; exch.

292   Univ. of Nebraska Libraries, Map Collection, zone 8.
      Mrs. Charlotte Ratcliffe, Science Librarian.
      Staff: 1 p-t.
      Areas: worldwide, Nebraska.
      Subjects: topography, geology, aerial photographs.
      Size: map sheets 38,000 (of which 25,000 are AMS deposi-
        tory; 10,000 sheets housed in the Depts. of Geology and
        Geography and the Division of Conservation and Survey);
        atlases 143 vol., 121 titles; globes 1; air photos 8,580.
      Serves faculty, students, public. Iln., photo.

NEVADA

CARSON CITY

293 Nevada Dept. of Highways.
      H.D. Mills, State Highway Engineer.
      Orvis E. Reil, Manager, Planning Survey.
      Dept. has extensive collection of maps which are used as
         reference guides in the construction of its various map
         series. State and county maps for sale include base
         maps and maps showing highways, traffic flow, school
         bus routes.

RENO

294 Univ. of Nevada.
      Mary F. Alvey.
      Staff: 1 p-t.
      Areas: the West, Nevada.
      Subjects: geology.
      Size: map sheets 30,000; atlases 45 vol., 40 titles.
      Serves faculty and students. Phst.

NEW HAMPSHIRE

CONCORD

295 Concord Public Library.
      T.E. Leberge, Reference Librarian.
      Staff: Reference Librarian and Assistant Reference
        Librarian work with maps only incidentally.
      Areas: New Hampshire, Concord.
      Subjects: local history.
      Size: map sheets 302; atlases 24 vol., 20 titles; globes 2.
      Serves public. Commercial phst.

296 New Hampshire Dept. of Public Works and Highways.
      George W. Harris, Survey Engineer.
      Staff: 4; 2 p-t.
      Areas: New Hampshire.
      Subjects: highways, bridges.
      Size: map sheets 60.
      Serves public. Blue line prints, photo-offset prints in
        few cases.

NEW HAMPSHIRE

CONCORD

297 New Hampshire Historical Society, Park St.
  Charlotte D. Conover, Librarian.
  Areas: early United States, New England, New Hampshire.
    Maps of townships of New Hampshire comprise more than
    half of the collection.
  Subjects: various.
  Size: 800-900 map sheets; atlases 30-40 vol., 30 titles;
    globes 3.
  Serves members and public. Commercial reproductions; exch.

298 New Hampshire State Library.
  Mrs. Mildred P. McKay, Librarian.
  Areas: New Hampshire (state government maps and survey
    quadrangles).
  Size: limited.

DURHAM

299 Univ. of New Hampshire Library.
  Mary Jean Donald, Reference Librarian.
  No special map collection with the exception of a quite
    complete USGS map set housed in the Geology Dept.

HANOVER

300 Dartmouth College Library, Map Dept.
  George R. Dalphin, Map Librarian.
  Staff: 1; 4 p-t; specialists available: geographers,
    cartographers, translators, faculty.
  Areas: worldwide, particularly, Arctic, Canada, U.S.S.R.,
    United States, New England, and New Hampshire.
  Subjects: agriculture, geology, historical cartography,
    local history, oceanography, topography, transportation.
  Size: map sheets 52,000; atlases 700 vol., 660 titles;
    globes 8; models 12; air photos, few local; photos of
    large relief models, 72.
  Serves faculty, students, public. Iln., phst., photo.,
    exch. Excel in Arctic due to presence of Vilhjalmur
    Stefansson Arctic Collection. Have Library of Congress
    Bibliography of Cartography on microfilm.

NEW HAMPSHIRE

300 (continued)
   Publications: Marine Atlases in the Dartmouth College
   Library, a descriptive list. 1950. Occasional
   articles in the Dartmouth College Library Bulletin.

MANCHESTER

301 City Library.
   Mrs. Betty Garst.
   Staff: 1 p-t.
   Areas: New England states.
   Size: map sheets 1,000; atlases 35 vol.; globes 2.
   Serves public.

302 Manchester Historic Association, 129 Amherst St.
   Howard A. Chamberlen, Curator.
   Areas: Manchester.
   Subjects: local.
   Size: map sheets 30; atlases 3 vol.
   Serves members and public.

NEW JERSEY

BLOOMFIELD

303 Free Public Library of Bloomfield, 90 Broad St.
   Dorothy M. Eadie, Reference Librarian.
   Staff: 1 p-t.
   Subjects: local history.
   Size: map sheets 203; atlases 34 vol., 32 titles.
   Serves public.

CONVENT STATION

304 General Drafting Co., Inc.
   Paul B. Lee, Assistant to the President.
   L.W. Spach, Librarian.
   Staff: 1; specialists available: cartographers.
   Areas: United States, Canada, Latin America, Europe, Asia.
   Subjects: transportation, travel.
   Size: map sheets 90,000; atlases 60 vol.
   Serves organization. Phst.

NEW JERSEY

EAST ORANGE

305 East Orange Free Public Library, 291 Main St.
     Staff: p-t.
     Areas: worldwide, New Jersey.
     Subjects: geology, history.
     Size: map sheets 2,236 in main library and 3 branches;
        atlases 50 vol. in main library; globes 1.
     Serves public.

ELIZABETH

306 Free Public Library.
     Helen J. Ferguson, Principal Reference and Technical
        Librarian.
     Staff: 1 p-t.
     Subjects: local history, geology.
     Size: map sheets 8,378; atlases 256 vol. (includes 236
        geological); globes 1.
     Serves public.

MAPLEWOOD

307 C.S. Hammond & Co., 515 Valley St.
     Martin A. Bacheller, Editor.
     Staff: 2 p-t.
     Areas: worldwide.
     Subjects: various.
     Size: map sheets 6,000; atlases 200 vol., 200 titles.
     Serves organization. Published maps and atlases are for
        sale. Catalog available on request.

NEW BRUNSWICK

308 Rutgers Univ. Library.
     Donald A. Sinclair, Curator of Special Collections.
     Staff: 2 p-t; specialists available: geographers,
        translators.
     Areas: United States, New Jersey.
     Subjects: geology, local history, topography.
     Size: map sheets 40,100; atlases 700 vol., 500 titles.
     Serves faculty, students, public. Iln., phst., photo.,
        micro., exch.

NEW JERSEY

NEWARK

309 New Jersey Historical Society, 230 Broadway, zone 4.
Areas: New Jersey.
Subjects: local and state history.
Size: map sheets 600; atlases 50 vol.
Serves organization and public. Phst., exch.

310 Newark Public Library, 5 Washington St., zone 1.
Bradley W. Leonard, Principal Librarian, Lending and
Reference Dept.
Size: map sheets including air photos 28,178; atlases
250 titles; globes 10.
Serves public. Commercial phst. and photo. Maps are not
centralized in one collection, but are found in several
depts. and branches. No one is in charge of all the maps.

PRINCETON

311 Princeton Univ. Library.
Mrs. Hanna Fanta-Fantova.
Staff: p-t.
Subjects: various, geology in Guyot Hall Library.
Size: map sheets 30,000; globes 1; air photos, few.
Serves univ. and public. Iln., phst., exch.

TRENTON

312 Free Public Library, Academy St., zone 5.
Mary T. Messler, Head, Reference Dept.
Staff: p-t.
Areas: worldwide, New Jersey, Pennsylvania, Mercer County,
N.J., Berks County, Pa., Trenton.
Subjects: history, geology, local history.
Size: map sheets 100; atlases 70 vol.; globes 1; air
photos, few.
Serves public. Iln., commercial phst. Reference staff
of 8 handle the maps; one person in charge of indexing
them. Historical maps are part of the Trentoniana
Collection.

NEW JERSEY

TRENTON

313 New Jersey State Dept. of Education, Division of the State
Library, Archives and History, State House Annex, zone 7.
Roger H. McDonough, Director.
Robert Malone, Reference Librarian.
Staff: 1 p-t.
Areas: New Jersey, state, counties, cities.
Subjects: history, geology.
Size: map sheets 6,450; atlases 365 vol., 350 titles.
Serves public. Iln., phst., exch.

314 State Teachers College, zone 5.
Adelbert K. Botts, Professor of Geography.
Staff: 1 p-t; specialists available: geographers.
Areas: New Jersey.
Subjects: various.
Size: map sheets 20,000; atlases 94 vol.. 76 titles;
globes 6; models 15; air photos 100.
Serves organization. Iln., phst., exch.

VINELAND

315 Vineland Historical and Antiquarian Society, 108 S. 7th St.
Elena J. Darling, Secretary.
Staff: p-t.
Areas: United States, New Jersey, Vineland.
Subjects: topography, geology, local history.
Size: map sheets, most of USGS; globes 3.
Serves normal school students. Phst., commercial photo.
Publications: Ankenbrand, Frank, Jr. "A Bibliography of
Vineland Maps Published and Original." Vineland Histor-
ical Magazine, vol. 23, p. 134.

NEW MEXICO

SANTA FE

316 New Mexico State Highway Dept., Planning Division, Box 1461.
H.S. Wiley, Planning Director.
Dept. does not maintain a map library, but has available at
cost maps published by the Dept.

NEW YORK

ALBANY

317 New York State Library, Manuscripts and History Section.
    Edna L. Jacobsen, Associate Librarian.
    Staff: 3 p-t.
    Areas: early America, United States, New York State.
    Subjects: history, topography, state planning, highways.
    Size: map sheets 50,000; atlases 800 vol.; globes 1;
      air photos, few.
    Serves state depts., public. Iln. within the state; phst.,
      small photo., exch.

BROOKLYN

318 Brooklyn Public Library, History Division, Grand Army Plaza,
    zone 38.
    Theodore P. Peck.
    Staff: 1 p-t.
    Areas: United States, New York State, Brooklyn.
    Subjects: history of the United States, local history,
      topography.
    Size: map sheets 4,000; atlases 315 vol., 259 titles.
    Serves public. Iln. Atlases cataloged; sheet maps
      indexed.

319 Long Island Historical Society, 128 Pierrepont St., zone 1.
    Edna Huntington, Librarian.
    Areas: Long Island.
    Subjects: local history.
    Size: map sheets 955; atlases 190; air photos, few.
    Serves organization and public. Exch. for maps of Long
      Island.

320 Chas. Pfizer & Co., Inc., Business Library, 11 Bartlett St.,
    zone 6.
    Muriel Carabba.
    Areas: United States, Canada.
    Subjects: marketing, sales and territory divisions by pri-
      mary areas, county and state.
    Size: map sheets 75; globes 2. Phst. Map Collection is
      part of the Business Library which was established under
      the Market Research Dept. and serves all depts. of the
      organization.

NEW YORK

BUFFALO

321 Buffalo Historical Society, Delaware Park, zone 7.
     Alice J. Pickup, Librarian.
     Areas: New York State, Erie County, Buffalo.
     Subjects: local history.
     Size: map sheets 200; atlases 30 vol., 15 titles.
     Serves organization and public. Phst., photographers
        permitted, exch.

322 Buffalo Public Library, Reference Dept., Lafayette Square,
     zone 3.
     Richard T. Morris, Assistant Director.
     Areas: worldwide.
     Subjects: various, including topographical, pictorial,
        political maps and navigation charts.
     Size: map sheets 25,000; atlases 200 vol.; globes 2;
        models 1.
     Serves public. Commercial reproductions only. AMS
        depository.

CLINTON

323 Hamilton College Library.
     Staff: 1 p-t; specialist available: Head of Geology Dept.
     Areas: United States and possessions.
     Subjects: geology.
     Size: map sheets 4,028; atlases 150 vol.
     Serves faculty, students, public. Iln. atlases; phst.;
        photo.

CORTLAND

324 Cortland County Historical Society, Court House.
     Mrs. D.N. Elder, Executive Secretary.
     Staff: 1 p-t.
     Areas: New York State, Cortland County and city.
     Subjects: local history, topography.
     Size: map sheets 50; atlases 5 vol.
     Serves organization and public. Public may send photo-
        graphers; exch.

NEW YORK

ENDICOTT

25 Harpur College.
    Specialists available: geographers.
    Areas: worldwide.
    Subjects: various.
    Size: map sheets 700.
    Serves organization.

ITHACA

26 Armand L. Adams, private collector, 504 Seneca Bldg.
    Areas: New York State, Tompkins County, Ithaca.
    Subjects: local history, land titles; especially Revolu-
      tionary land bounties covering period from 1780-1840.
    Size: map sheets 1,000; atlases 10; air photos 400, local
      history texts 100.
    Serves owner and others interested in local history. Iln.

27 Cornell Univ. Library.
    Burbura Burtholsen, Map Librarian
    Staff: 1; 1 p-t; specialists available: faculty in geology,
      civil engineering, and modern languages depts.
    Areas: Far East, China (Wason Far East Collection), New
      York State.
    Subjects: city planning, geology, local and regional
      history, land use, and political and physical maps
      suitable for classroom use.
    Size: map sheets 39,425; atlases 600 vol., 500 titles;
      globes 2; photos 5,100.
    Serves faculty, students, public. Iln., phst., photo.,
      micro., exch.

JAMAICA

28 Queens Borough Public Library, 89-14 Parsons Blvd., zone 32.
    Marguerite V. Doggett, Librarian, Long Island Collection.
    Staff: 2.
    Areas: Long Island.
    Subjects: various.
    Size: map sheets 5,000; atlases 37 vol.
    Serves public. Commercial reproductions only.

NEW ROCHELLE

329   New Rochelle Public Library, 662 Main St.
      Jean Ross, Reference Librarian.
      Areas: Westchester County, New Rochelle.
      Size: map sheets 50; atlases 40 vols., 40 titles;
        globes 1.
      Serves public.

NEW YORK

330   American Automobile Association, International Travel Dept.,
      250 Park Ave., zone 17.
      Elise Phillips, Director of Research.
      Serves public. Maintains a reference collection of foreign
        road maps. Distribution copies for sale.

331   American Broadcasting Company, General Library, 7 West 66th
      St., zone 23.
      Ruth M. Crawford, Librarian.
      Staff: p-t; specialists available: geographers.
      Areas: worldwide, United States.
      Subjects: history, place-names.
      Size: map sheets 50; atlases 3 vol.
      Serves organization. Exch. American Broadcasting Co.,
        Map Dept. makes some maps concerned with radio, TV,
        sales, and population. Television News Dept. adapts
        its own maps for special uses.

332   American Geographical Society, Map Dept., Broadway at 156th
      St., zone 32.
      Ena L. Yonge, Map Curator.
      Staff: 3; 2 p-t; specialists available: geographers,
        cartographers, translators.
      Areas: worldwide.
      Subjects: various, well rounded, all types and scales.
      Size: map sheets 230,000; atlases 3,000 titles; globes
        20; air photos, few; models, several.
      Serves public. Iln., phst., public may send photographers,
        exch. Collection completely cataloged by area, subject,
        author. Cards for maps in books and periodicals in the
        Library are added to the map catalog.

NEW YORK

332   (continued)
Publications: Manual for the Classification and Cataloging
of Maps in the Society's Collection. 1952. (Mimeographed
& Offset Publication no. 4). Current Geographical Pub-
locations, monthly except July and August.

333   American Overseas Petroleum Limited, (California-Texas Oil
Co.), 551 Fifth Ave., zone 17.
Hope A. Kingman, Librarian.
Staff: 1.
Areas: Eastern Hemisphere.
Subjects: geology, topography.
Size: map sheets 2,000 plus complete coverage of WAC charts
for Eastern Hemisphere; atlases 8 vol.
Serves organization. Iln. This new map collection is part
of a geological and geophysical library.

334   City College, 140th Street & St. Nicholas Terrace, zone 31.
Jerome K. Wilcox, Librarian.
Hilde Werthauer.
Size: map sheets 700; atlases 150 folios of Geologic Atlas
of the United States.
Serves faculty, students.

335   Columbia Univ. Geology Library and Map Room, 601 Schermerhorn
Hall, zone 27.
Francis O'Leary, Librarian.
Edward Brandon, Map Librarian.
Staff: 1; specialists available: faculty.
Areas: worldwide, North America.
Subjects: petroleum geology, topography.
Size: map sheets 49,000; atlases 80 titles; globes 3; air
photos, few.
Serves faculty and students. Phst., photo., micro., exch.
Depository for AMS and USGS. Additional atlases in other
dept. libraries of the univ.

336   Cowles Magazines, Inc., 488 Madison Ave., zone 22.
W.J. Burke, Librarian.
Areas: United States.
Subjects: transportation.
Size: map sheets 300; atlases 15.
Serves organization.

NEW YORK

338 Frick Art Reference Library, 10 East 71st St., zone 21.
Mrs. Hannah Johnson Howell, Librarian.
The Library maintains an extensive collection of guide
books on western Europe and the Americas from the ear-
liest published to date. Many maps are included in
these guides.

339 Richard Edes Harrison, private collector and cartographer,
313 East 51st St., zone 22.
Staff: 3 p-t; specialists available: cartographer,
specialist in map typography.
Areas: worldwide.
Subjects: shaded relief; oblique projections.
Size: map sheets 1,000; atlases 75 vol.; globes 6;
models 1.
Serves owner's private cartographic studio and public.
Limited iln., commercial reproduction, exch.
Collection has been accumulated almost solely as a working instrument for the production of maps.
Collection contains a fairly extensive group of projections (grids) and sketch maps. Many are in manuscript
form and not readily available elsewhere. Especially
strong in oblique cases of the azimuthal equidistant
and orthographic projections.

340 Hispanic Society of America, Broadway between 155th and
156th Sts., zone 32.
Adelaide M. Meyer, Chairman, General Staff Committee.
Areas: Spain, Portugal, South and Central America.
Size: 42 manuscript maps (including 32 portolan charts)
by Catalan, French, German and Italian cartographers;
additional printed maps; globes 27.
Serves public. Photographs of edited material available.
Publications: Hispanic Society of America. Catalogue of
Publications, by Clara L. Penney. New York, 1943.
Lists map studies.

NEW YORK

NEW YORK

341 Hunter College, Dept. of Geology & Geography, 695 Park Ave.,
     zone 21.
     Staff: 2 p-t; specialists available: geographers, carto-
        graphers, geologists.
     Areas: worldwide, United States, Canada.
     Subjects: topography, geology, aeronautics, conservation,
        meteorology, navigation.
     Size: map sheets 21,000; atlases 675 vol., 12 titles and
        226 U.S. geologic folios; globes 13; models 115; air
        photos 116.
     Serves faculty, students.

342 Municipal Reference Library, Rm. 2230, Municipal Bldg.,
     zone 7.
     Areas: New York City.
     Subjects: real estate, elections.
     Size: map sheets 300; atlases 75 vol., 40 titles;
        globes 1.
     Serves public.

343 The New York Enthusiasts, 939 Eighth Ave., zone 19.
     Hans Hacker.
     Areas: New York motopolitan area.
     Subjects: local history.
     Size: map sheets 400; atlases 20.
     Serves organization.

344 New York Historical Society, 170 Central Park West, zone 24.
     Arthur B. Carlson, Curator, Map and Print Room.
     Staff: 2.
     Areas: United States, New York State, New York City.
     Subjects: local history, real estate, transportation.
     Size: map sheets 75,000; atlases 1,225 vol.; globes 1.
     Serves public. Phst.; photo.; micro.; exch.
     Collection contains the Erskine-DeWitt manuscript maps of
        the American Revolution.

NEW YORK

345 New York Public Library, Map Division, Fifth Ave. & 42nd St.,
     zone 18.
     Gerald D. McDonald, Chief, American History Division,
     Acting Chief Map Division.
     Staff: 4; 2 p-t; specialists available: cartographers,
     geographers.
     Areas: worldwide.
     Subjects: various.
     Size: map sheets 210,000; atlases 4,500; globes 5;
     samples of models and air photos.
     Serves public. Phst., photo., micro., exch. The collec-
     tion is particularly strong in rare 16th, 17th, 18th
     Century atlases and maps; in the history of cartography;
     techniques of map making, as well as United States county
     atlases and real estate atlases. The Library houses the
     map collections assembled by James Lenox, I.N. Phelps
     Stokes, and others. The entire collection is cataloged
     by area, subject, and author. The catalog has references
     to many important maps found elsewhere in the Library.
     A Bibliography of atlases, books and articles on maps is
     maintained.
     Publications: Occasional lists, articles and bibliographical
     studies in the Library's Bulletin.

346 Pierpont Morgan Library, 29 East 36th St., zone 16.
     Library has no special map collection. Among examples of
     medieval manuscripts and specimens of early printing are
     a number of items of cartographical interest, the most
     important of which are mentioned in the following pub-
     lications:
     L.C. Wroth, The Early Cartography of the Pacific. New
     York, Bibliographical Society of America, 1944.
     Baltimore Museum of Art. The World Encompassed, An
     Exhibition of the History of Maps . . . Baltimore, 1952.
     Phst., photo.

347 Regional Plan Association, Inc., 205 E. 42nd St., zone 17.
     George A. Schiller.
     Staff: 1 p-t; specialists available by appointment.
     Areas: New York metropolitan region.

NEW YORK

347 (continued)
     Subjects: various.
     Size: map sheets not est.; atlases 10 vol.; air photos 50.
     Serves staff and members. Commercial phst. Research file
       contains numerous manuscript maps and charts compiled by
       the staff in connection with regional studies. These
       maps on varying scales show land development, population,
       distribution, transportation, industrial location.

348 Socony-Vacuum Oil Co. Inc., Room 737, 26 Broadway, zone 4.
     P. de Freitas, Geology Librarian, A. MacRae, Map Room.
     Staff: 2 p-t.
     Areas: worldwide.
     Subjects: geology, petroleum industry.
     Size: map sheets 7,000; atlases 10 vol.; globes 1; air
       photos 200.
     Serves organization. Phst., photo., contact prints.

349 Standard-Vacuum Oil Co., Exploration-Producing Dept. Map
     Library, 26 Broadway, zone 4.
     Genevieve M. Kushnir.
     Staff: 1.
     Areas: Pacific and Indian oceans.
     Subjects: geology.
     Size: map sheets 2,000; atlases 2; air photos 30,000.
     Serves organization.

350 Stewart, Dougall & Associate, Inc., 30 Rockefeller Plaza,
     zone 20.
     Bonnie Lou Rickey, Librarian.
     Staff: p-t.
     Areas: United States.
     Subjects: state road maps, transportation, city street
       plans.
     Size: map sheets 1,200; atlases 6 vol.
     Serves organization and clients. Iln.

351 United Nations Map Collection.
     Nathaniel Abelson, Map Librarian.
     Staff: 1; 1 p-t; specialists available: geographers,
       cartographers, translators, U.N. Secretariat.
     Areas: worldwide.

NEW YORK

351   (continued)
        Subjects: boundaries, topography, transportation, re-
        sources, population, place names.
        Size: map sheets 45,000; atlases 400 titles; globes 1.
        Serves organization. Phst., photo., ozalid light table
        for internal use only; exch. The collection contains
        550 gazetteers which are considered indispensable.
        Also located in the Map Collection are technical books
        on geography, cartography, sailing directions, guide
        books and travel publications.

352   Wenner-Gren Foundation for Anthropological Research, Inc.,
        14 E. 71st St., zone 21.
        Emil Vernei, Research Librarian.
        Areas: worldwide.
        Subjects: anthropology including ethnology, archeology,
        linguistics.
        Size: map sheets 250; atlases 10; air photos 5,000.
        Serves organization. Photo. Most important holding is
        Shipee-Johnson collection of aerial photographs of
        Peru, of special interest to archeologists. Collec-
        tion consists principally of copies or originals of
        maps prepared by research scholars subsidized by the
        Foundation.

      PEEKSKILL

353   City of Peekskill Historical Library, Municipal Building.
        William T. Horton, City Historian.
        Staff: 2 p-t.
        Areas: Peekskill & contiguous territory; i.e., Southern
        Putnam and Northern Westchester from Hudson River to
        Connecticut line.
        Subjects: local history, topography, transportation.
        Size: map sheets 300; atlases 6 vol.
        Serves public. Iln., phst., photo.

NEW YORK

POUGHKEEPSIE

354   Dutchess County Historical Society.
      Mrs. H. Stecholm, Curator.
      Staff: 1 p-t (volunteer).
      Areas: Dutchess County.
      Subjects: local history.
      Size: map sheets 20; atlases 3 vols; air photos 4.
      Serves public.

355   Vassar College Library.
      Eileen Thornton, Librarian.
      Size: map sheets 750; atlases 265 vol.; 190 titles;
         globes 1.
      Serves faculty and students.
      The Lasker collection includes twelve rare atlases ranging
         in date from 1572 to 1778; three portfolios of maps
         chiefly of the 16th, 17th, and 18th Centuries and a few
         modern pieces.   Additional maps in the depts. of history,
         geography, and geology.

ROCHESTER

356   Rochester Public Library, 155 South Ave., zone 4.
      Areas: New York State, Rochester, Genesee Valley.
      Subjects: picture maps, local history, geology, World
         War II.
      Size: map sheets 5,077; atlases 214 vol., titles 180;
         globes 2.
      Serves public.   Phst.   Maps are divided between the follow-
         ing divisions: General Reference, Local History, History
         and Travel, Science and Technology.

SYRACUSE

357   Syracuse Public Library, 335 Montgomery St., zone 2.
      Areas: worldwide; Syracuse and Onondaga County.
      Subjects: various and local history.
      Size: map sheets 1,750; atlases 70 (plus 225 folios of
         of Geologic Atlas of the U.S.); globes 1.
      Serves public.   Tln.

NEW YORK

SYRACUSE

358 Syracuse Univ., Lyman Hall Library, zone 10.
Mrs. Jessie Watkins, Map Librarian.
Staff: 2 p-t; specialists available: geographers, carto-
graphers, translators.
Areas: worldwide.
Subjects: various.
Size: map sheets 27,000; atlases 75 vol., 71 titles;
globes 2.
Serves faculty and students. Iln., phst. Depository for
AMS, USGS and Canadian Geological Survey. Special
regional classification adapted from the U.S. Office of
Strategic Services is used; separate map catalogs,
regional and subject, are maintained. Additional
stlases are part of the Main Univ. Library.

WEST POINT

358a U.S. Military Academy, Library.
Staff: 5 p-t.
Areas: worldwide.
Subjects: local history.
Size: map sheets 4,336; atlases 410 vol.; globes 2.
Serves organization. Phst. Maps of special interest in
the collection include:
1. Original maps from the Confederate Engineer Bureau,
Gen. J.F. Gilmer, chief engineer. (42 maps of
Virginia campaigns.) 1861 ? - 1865.
2. Twenty-two maps chiefly on the American Revolution
by William Faden, 1750-1836.

NORTH CAROLINA

CHAPEL HILL

359 Univ. of North Carolina Library, Map Room.
Olan V. Cook, Assistant Librarian.
Staff: 1 p-t; specialists available: geographers.
Areas: southern part of the United States, North Carolina.
Subjects: topography, city planning, state and local his-
tory, geology.

NORTH CAROLINA

359 (continued)
Size: map sheets 50,525 (includes AMS depository);
atlases 25 vol.
Serves faculty, students, public. Iln., phst., photo.,
micro., exch.

DURHAM

360 Duke Univ. Library.
Wilhelmina Lemen, Documents Librarian.
Staff: 1 p-t.
Areas: southeastern United States.
Subjects: local history.
Size: map sheets 12,150; atlases 181 vol., 151 titles.
Serves faculty, students, public in accord with library
policy. Iln., photoprints, exch.

FORT BRAGG

361 Joint Tactical Air Support Board Library.
Charles P. Cellle, Jr., Librarian.
Staff: 1 p-t; specialists available: officers trained in
map reading.
Size: map sheets 300; atlases 125 vol.; air photos 10.
Serves organization. The requirements of this Board for
maps is very limited.

RALEIGH

362 North Carolina Dept. of Archives and History, Box 1881.
W. Frank Burton, State Archivist.
Staff: 1; 3 p-t.
Areas: North Carolina.
Size: map sheets 2,000; atlases 15 vol.
Serves state government, public. Phst., micro.

NORTH DAKOTA

BISMARCK

363   North Dakota State Highway Dept.
      R. E. Bradley, Road Design Engineer.
      Areas: North Dakota.
      Subjects: transportation.
      Size: map sheets not est.;
      Serves organization and public. Phst. Maps of the state
         and its counties, published by the Dept. are for sale.

364   State Historical Society of North Dakota, Liberty Memorial
      Bldg.
      Margaret Rose.
      Staff: 1 p-t.
      Areas: upper midwest and adjacent Canadian provinces,
         North Dakota.
      Subjects: local history, transportation, exploration and
         early travel, military expeditions.
      Size: map sheets 900; atlases 80 vol.
      Serves organization, state offices, public. Phst., exch.

VALLEY CITY

'365 State Teachers College Library.   Army Surplus Map Library.
      Ina C. Robertson.
      Staff: 1.
      Areas: worldwide.
      Subjects: topographic, political, economic, transportation.
      Size: map sheets 25,000 (AMS); atlases 10 vol.; globes 2;
         models 3.
      Serves college and public. Iln., phst.

OHIO

ATHENS

366   Ohio Univ. Library.
      Frank N. Jones, Reference Librarian.
      Specialists available: faculty.
      Areas: United States.
      Size: map sheets 250-350; atlases 30 vol.,   titles 27;
         globes 1.
      Serves faculty, students and public.

OHIO

CINCINNATI

367 Historical and Philosophical Society of Ohio, Univ. of Cin-
cinnati Library Building, zone 21.
Mrs. Alice P. Hook, Librarian.
Areas: western waters to 1787, Northwest Territory, Ohio,
Cincinnati.
Subjects: local history, state history.
Size: map sheets 1,100-1,200; atlases 140 vol., 140 titles;
also many early travel books.
Serves historical research students and public. Commercial
reproductions only. Exch.

368 Public Library of Cincinnati and Hamilton County, 629 Vine
St., zone 2.
Rosemary Martin, Assistant, Reference Department.
Staff: 1 p-t.
Areas: Ohio, Hamilton County, Cincinnati.
Size: map sheets 55,000; atlases 450 titles; globes 1;
relief models 3.
Serves public. Commercial reproductions only, exch.

369 Univ. of Cincinnati Library, zone 21.
Lorraine B. Hess, Assistant in charge of Army Maps &
Geology Library.
Staff: 1 p-t; specialists available: geographers, carto-
graphers.
Areas: worldwide.
Subjects: geology, topography.
Size: map sheets 38,100; atlases 45 vol.; models 15.
Serves faculty, students, public. AMS depository and
reference atlases are housed in General Library, others
in Geology Library.

CLEVELAND

370 Cleveland College of Western Reserve Univ., Library, Public
Square, zone 14.
Specialists available: faculty.
Areas: worldwide.
Size: map sheets 250; atlases 46 vol., 42 titles; globes 2.
Serves organization. Iln.

OHIO

CLEVELAND

371 Cleveland Public Library, 325 Superior Ave., zone 14
   Florence M. Gifford, Head, General Reference Division.
   Staff: 2 p-t; specialists available: translators.
   Areas: Great Lakes area, Caribbean area of Latin
   America, Cleveland, Ohio, and contiguous states
   are emphasized.
   Subjects: local history, early travel in Great Lakes
   region, geology of Middle West.
   Size: map sheets 10,000 plus AMS maps; atlases 900
   titles, including portfolios of map sheets; globes
   4; models 3; air photos 2.
   Serves public. Iln., phst., photo., micro., exch.
   AMS depository.

COLUMBUS

372 Ohio State Archaeological and Historical Society, 15th
   and N. High St.
   Elizabeth C. Biggert, Manuscript Librarian.
   Staff: p-t.
   Areas: middle western United States, Ohio.
   Subjects: history, local history.
   Size: map sheets 2,600; atlases 544 vol., 400 titles.
   Serves research staff and public. Iln., phst., photo.,
   micro., exch.

373 Ohio State Univ. Libaries, Map Library, zone 10.
   Staff: 1; 1 p-t; specialists available: geographers,
   cartographers.
   Areas: worldwide, South America, Europe, United States,
   Ohio.
   Subjects: geography, transportation, economics.
   Size: map sheets 53,500; atlases 24; globes 1.
   Serves faculty, students, public. Iln., phst., photo.,
   micro., exch. Hundreds of additional atlases kept
   in stacks.
   Publications: Library Handbook of the Ohio State Univer-
   sity, 1952.

OHIO

DAYTON

74 Dayton Public Library, 215 E. Third St., zone 2.
Areas: Montgomery County, surrounding counties, Dayton.
Subjects: local history.
Size: map sheets 63; atlases 17 vol., 17 titles; air
photos 4.
Serves public. Iln., commercial reproduction only.

DELAWARE

75 Ohio Wesleyan Univ., Charles E. Slocum Library.
John H. Reed, Reference Librarian.
Areas: western Hemisphere, United States.
Subjects: geology.
Size: map sheets 300; atlases 30 vol.; globes 2;
models 3.
Serves organization, AFROTC.

GRANVILLE

76 Denison Univ. William Howard Doane Library.
Richard Mahard, Associate Professor of Geology.
Specialists available: geographers.
Areas: United States.
Subjects: geology.
Size: map sheets 85% of topographic quadrangles before
1940.
Serves organization and public. Phst., contoura.

KENT

77 Kent State Univ., Dept. of Geography & Geology.
H.F. Raup, Head of Dept.
Specialists available: geographers, cartographers, geologists.
Areas: Canada, Ohio.
Subjects: geology, local history, transportation, land use,
cities, county engineers' maps.
Size: map sheets 200 plus; atlases 50 vol.; globes 6;
models 12.
Serves faculty, students, public. Iln., phst., exch.

OHIO

OBERLIN

378 Oberlin College.
     Reuel B. Frost.
     Staff: 1 p-t; specialists available: geographers,
       translators.
     Areas: Europe, United States.
     Subjects: various.
     Size: map sheets 60,000; atlases 367 vol., titles 250;
       globes 34; models, several; air photos, few.
     Serves faculty, students, and public with restrictions.
     Phst., photo.

TOLEDO

379 Toledo Public Library, 325 Michigan St., zone 2.
     Samuel S. McConoughey, Head, Reference Dept.
     Staff: 2 p-t.
     Areas: worldwide, Toledo.
     Subjects: local history.
     Size: map sheets 17,500 plus USGS; atlases 102 vol., 70
       titles; globes 1.
     Serves public. Iln., phst., micro., exch. AMS depository
       cataloged.

YELLOW SPRINGS

380 Antioch College.
     Ruth F. Bent, Science Librarian.
     Specialists available: geographers, cartographers, transla-
       tors.
     Areas: Europe, United States.
     Subjects: geology, geography.
     Size: map sheets 50,000; atlases 30 vol., 25 titles;
       globes 2; relief models 3; air photos 20.
     Serves organization. Iln., Remington-Rand Photocopier,
       Contoura, exch. AMS depository. Map room to be provided
       in future; present lack of space and equipment limits use
       to Earth Science Dept.

OKLAHOMA

NORMAN

380a Univ. of Oklahoma, Dept. of Geography, Map Library.
Harry E. Hoy.
Staff: 1 p-t; specialists available: geographers,
cartographers.
Areas: worldwide; heavy concentration on World War II
theatres and potential theatres of action.
Size: map sheets 100,000; atlases 150 vol., 35 titles;
globes 4; models 30; air photos 1,000.
Serves geography Dept. primarily, also public. Iln. of
duplicates, exch.

380b Univ. of Oklahoma, Geological Library.
Mrs. Lucy Finnerty, Librarian.
Staff: 1 p-t; specialists available: geological faculty
and staff of Oklahoma Geological Survey.
Areas: Europe, South America, United States, Canada,
Oklahoma, Kansas, Texas, Arkansas, Missouri.
Subjects: topography, geology, oil and gas fields,
minerals, cross-sections, correlation charts.
Size: map sheets 15,476; atlases 489 vol., 265 titles.
Serves faculty, students, public, staff of Oklahoma
Geological Survey. Iln., exch.

380c Univ. of Oklahoma Library, Division of Manuscripts; and the
Frank Phillips Collection, Materials on Western History.
James M. Babcock, Acting Archivist.
Don Rickey, Phillips Collection Librarian.
Staff: 1 p-t; librarian is specialist in western history.
Areas: Southwestern United States, Indian Reservations,
Oklahoma, Indian Territory.
Subjects: local history, with emphasis on relations to
Indians and frontier.
Size: map sheets 673; atlases 17 vol., 3 titles.
Serves Depts. of History, Anthropology, Sociology, Eco-
nomics, and Government; public; researchers in western
Americana. Exch.

OKLAHOMA

OKLAHOMA CITY

381 Muldrow Aerial Surveys Corporation, 208 N.W. Fifth St.,
     zone 3.
       Richard T. Garrison, Comptroller.
       Staff: 25; specialists available: cartographers.
       Areas: North Dakota, South Dakota, Nebraska, Wyoming,
         Utah, Colorado, Kansas, Oklahoma, New Mexico, parts of
         Texas, Arizona, Idaho, Montana.
       Subjects: controlled regional base maps (surveys-land net).
       Size: map sheets 1,278.
       Serves oil industry. Phst., photo., direct prints, blue
         line prints, film. Muldrow Base Maps are drafted at a
         scale of 1" equals 4,000', in grids of 30 minutes of
         latitude and longitude. They are compiled from township
         plats and maps of government agencies. Aerial photo-
         graphy is used, along with Muldrow field ties to USGS
         and USCGS triangulation. The result is a land net suf-
         ficiently accurate for land and geophysical as well as
         geological purposes. The 4,000' scale may be enlarged
         to 1" equals 2,000' if desired.

381a Oklahoma City Libraries, 3rd and Robinson Sts.,
       Staff: 1 p-t; specialists available: translators.
       Areas: Latin America, United States, Canada, Alaska,
         Oklahoma.
       Subjects: geology, topography, local history.
       Size: map sheets 27,000; atlases 13 vol.
       Serves public. Iln., commercial reproductions, exch. Ap-
         proximately 1,000 map sheets are cataloged, others are
         listed in subject indexes.

382 State Dept. of Highways, Capitol Office Bldg.
       Gaines H. Stout, Engineer of Plans and Survey.
       Staff: 1; specialists available: draftsmen.
       Areas: Oklahoma.
       Subjects: town maps showing lots, blocks, streets, railroad
       Size: map sheets 200.
       Serves organization. Blue prints and black and white prints

OKLAHOMA

STILLWATER

82a Oklahoma Agricultural and Mechanical College Library, Map
Dept.
   Angie Debo, Curator of Maps.
   Staff: 1; 1 p-t; specialists available: geographers,
      cartographers, translators.
   Areas: worldwide, Oklahoma.
   Subjects: topography, geology, transportation, agri-
      culture, soils, local history.
   Size: map sheets 46,932; atlases 146 vol., 145 titles.
   Serves faculty, students, visiting scholars. Exch.
   Collection completely cataloged by area and subject.
   L.C. cards used in some instances, but not L.C.
   classification.

TULSA

83 Univ. of Tulsa Library, zone 4.
   Staff: 1 p-t; specialists available: geographers.
   Size: map sheets 8,000; atlases 68 vol.
   Serves organization and public. Iln., micro.

OREGON

CORVALLIS

84 Oregon State College Library, Reference Dept., Map Collection.
   Hazel Saremal.
   Specialists available: geographers, geologists, meteorol-
      ogists, translators.
   Areas: Oregon and the eleven most westerly states.
   Subjects: agriculture, geology, topography, meteorology,
      local history.
   Size: map sheets 37,056; atlases 84 vol., 60 titles;
      globes 1; air photos 118; historical weather maps 647 vol.
   Serves faculty, students, public, also the Agricultural
      Experiment Station and Extension Service. Iln., phst.,
      photo. AMS depository set includes captured German and
      Japanese maps. A collection of aerial photographic index
      maps of Oregon has been started. Map and atlas collections
      are cataloged by area, subject, and author except for the
      AMS set.

OREGON

EUGENE

385   Univ. of Oregon, Library.
      Edward P. Thatcher, Science Librarian.
      Staff: 1 p-t; specialists available: geographers,
        translators, faculty.
      Areas: United States, Pacific Northwest, Oregon.
      Subjects: Northwest exploration.
      Size: map sheets 39,266; atlases 50 titles; globes 1.
      Serves faculty, students, public. Iln.

PORTLAND

386   Library Association of Portland, 801 S.W. Tenth, zone 5.
      Elizabeth Anne Johnson.
      Areas: Pacific, Pacific Northwest, Oregon.
      Subjects: local history, USGS topographical sheets.
      Size: map sheets 5,000; atlases 100 vol.; globes 1;
        models 1.
      Serves public. Iln., commerical phst.

387   Oregon Historical Society Library, 235 S.W. Market St.,
      zone 1.
      Inez Haskell, Librarian.
      Areas: Pacific Northwest with emphasis on Oregon.
      Subjects: local history.
      Size: map sheets 1,500.
      Serves public. Phst., photo.

SALEM

388   Oregon State Library, State Library Bldg.
      Mary Keefer, Head, Catalog Division.
      Staff: 1 p-t; specialists available: translators.
      Areas: Pacific Northwest, Oregon.
      Subjects: geology, local history; official maps of the
        state and of the Railroad Commission of Oregon (in the
        Archives Division).
      Size: map sheets 1,515, exclusive of AMS and USGS deposi-
        tory sets; atlases 75 vol., 70 titles.
      Serves state officials and public. Iln., phst., micro.
      Publications: Some Historical Oregon Maps in the Oregon
        State Library, June, 1937. Mimeo.

PENNSYLVANIA

ALLENTOWN

389 Lehigh County Historical Society, Trout Hall.
Melville J. Boyer.
Staff: 1 p-t.
Areas: Lehigh County.
Subjects: early land drafts, settlement, local history.
Size: map sheets 50; atlases 6 vol., 6 titles.
Serves organization, public, local historians. Phst.,
photo. Map of Lehigh County of Isaac Chapman, pen and
ink, 1815, 54x70 in. has been restored and photographed
actual size. Cloth copies (prints) $25., paper $15.
Contains names of owners for whom surveys were made.

BETHLEHEM

390 Lehigh Univ. Library.
Staff: 1 p-t.
Areas: Amazon Valley, Canada, United States, Pennsylvania.
Subjects: local history, geology, topography, early
Americana.
Size: map sheets 1,200; atlases 50 vol., 50 titles;
globes 1.
Serves faculty, students, public. Iln., phst. Formal
collection is relatively new; figures are incomplete and
represent only maps already cataloged. The Library col-
lection is augmented by 3,000 sheets on geology and to-
pography in the Geology Dept.

BRYN MAWR

391 Bryn Mawr College.
Staff: 1 p-t; specialists available: cartographers.
Subjects: geology, topography.
Size: map sheets 72,000; globes 4; models 30; air photos
1,000.
Serves college community. Iln. AMS and USGS maps.

PENNSYLVANIA

CARLISLE BARRACKS

392 U.S. Army War College, Library.
Dorothy A. Wood. Map Librarian.
Staff: 1 p-t; area specialists on faculty.
Areas: Europe, Asia.
Subjects: topography.
Size: map sheets 20,000; atlases 25 vol., 25 titles;
globes 1; models 10.
Serves faculty, students, local R.O.T.C. and Army Reserve
Corps. Phst., photo., lithograph.

EASTON

393 Northampton County Historical and Genealogical Society,
4th and Ferry Sts.
Areas: Pennsylvania, Northampton County.
Subjects: local history.
Size: map sheets 10 (framed); atlases 50 vol.; air
photos 7.
Serves public. Society includes a museum.

HARRISBURG

394 Pennsylvania Bureau of Land Records, Dept. of Internal
Affairs, 543 Capitol Bldg.,
Warren J. Daniel, Director.
Areas: Pennsylvania; many manuscript maps covering state
boundaries, and land grants. Service to the public is
limited.

395 Pennsylvania Dept. of Highways.
Publishes maps of counties, cities, townships, boroughs,
and highways of the state.

396 Pennsylvania Historical and Museum Commission, Division of
Public Records, 221 Education Bldg.
Henry Howard Eddy, State Records Officer.
Areas: Pennsylvania.
Subjects: transportation; early state roads and turnpikes,
some canals.
Size: map sheets 1,000.
Serves public. Phst.

PENNSYLVANIA

HARRISBURG

97 Pennsylvania Historical and Museum Commission, Historical
    Division, State Museum Bldg.
    Donald H. Kent, Associate State Historian.
    Staff: 1 p-t; specialists available: translators.
    Areas: Pennsylvania.
    Subjects: state, county, and local.
    Size: map sheets 3,100 (includes phst. of maps relating
      to Pennsylvania from the beginning to 1830).
    Serves organization and public. Phst.

HONESDALE

398 Wayne County Historical Society, Delaware and Hudson Canal
    and Gravity Railroads Collection.
    Myrtle V. Newton, Secretary.
    Subjects: early transportation and local history.
    Serves public. Iln.

JENKINTOWN

399 Tall Tree Library, 253 Wyncote Road.
    George H. Beans, private collector.
    Staff: 1 p-t.
    Subjects: maps are according to schools and periods, not
      areas. Japanese Maps of the Tokugewa Era, 550 maps;
      Maps printed in Italy before A.D. 1600., 3,000 maps.
      Catalog entries are by individual maps. No record of
      number of atlases or volumes.
    Publications: Tall Tree Library Publications, nos., 1-23,
      descriptive brochure available on request.

KUTZTOWN

400 State Teachers College.
    Mrs. Mary Ellen Lewis, Librarian.
    Staff: 2 p-t; specialists available: geographers.
    Areas: Pennsylvania.
    Size: map sheets 213 on Pennsylvania, 100 topographic sheets
      on land features of United States; atlases 30 vol., 24
      titles.
    Serves college and teachers in service.

PENNSYLVANIA

LEWISBURG

401 Bucknell Univ., Ellen Clarke Bertrand Library.
     Mildred H. Bolich, Reference Librarian.
     Staff: 1 p-t; specialists available: geographers.
     Areas: worldwide, United States.
     Subjects: geology.
     Size: map sheets 1,500 (includes Army maps); atlases
        100 vol.; globes 1.
     Serves faculty and students. Phst., photo.

PHILADELPHIA

402 The Academy of Natural Sciences of Philadelphia, 19th St.
     and the Parkway, zone 3.
     Mrs. Venia T. Phillips, Librarian.
     Mary F. Pearsall, Periodicals Assistant (in charge of maps)
     Staff: 1 p-t; specialists available: geologists.
     Areas: worldwide.
     Subjects: geologic, political, relief.
     Size: map sheets 15,500; atlases 80 vol., 70 titles.
     Serves organization and public. Contoura. Complete sets
        of USGS topographic maps and Canadian Dept. of Mines
        and Resources, National topographic series.

403 Aero Service Corporation, 236 E. Courtland St., zone 20.
     George Hamlin, Jr.
     Staff: over 400. Specialists available: geographers,
        cartographers.
     Areas: worldwide.
     Subjects: topography, relief models, air photos.
     Size: models 16, air photos, several hundred thousand.
     Serves public. One of the largest commercial aerial map-
        ping organizations in the world. In addition to the air
        photos, photo-maps (or photo-mosaics) and topographic
        maps, Aero Service produces relief models for special
        requirements and teaching purposes.

404 Eastern Baptist Theological Seminary, Lancaster Ave. and
     City Line, zone 31.
     Areas: Bible lands.
     Subjects: history, particularly Biblical.
     Size: map sheets 125; atlases 20 vol., 19 titles.
     Serves organization.

PENNSYLVANIA

PHILADELPHIA

405 Franklin Institute of the State of Pennsylvania, Library,
zone 3.
Walter A. R. Pertuch, Librarian.
Size: map sheets 8,000, including topographical maps
published by the United States government.

406 Free Library of Philadelphia, Map Division, Logan Square,
zone 3.
Mrs. Helen M. F. White, Head.
Staff: 2; 1 p-t.
Areas: worldwide, Pennsylvania, Philadelphia.
Subjects: various.
Size: map sheets 67,800; atlases 2,180 vol.; globes 11;
models 1; air photos 573 (Philadelphia); geographic and
travel pamphlets 18,900. Does not include material in
Rare Book Room.
Serves public. Phst., photo. (small); exch. About two-
thirds of atlas collection is cataloged; maps are not
cataloged. AMS and USGS depository.

407 The Historical Society of Pennsylvania, 1300 Locust St.,
zone 4.
Harry Givens.
Staff: 3 p-t.
Areas: southeastern Pennsylvania, Philadelphia.
Subjects: local history.
Size: map sheets 3,500; atlases 400 vol.
Serves public. Phst., photo. Completely cataloged.

408 Library Company of Philadelphia, Ridgway Branch, Broad and
Christian Sts., zone 47.
Barney Chesnick, Assistant Librarian.
Areas: Europe, America.
Size: map sheets 1,200; atlases 560 vol., 470 titles.
Serves public. Iln., phst., photo. No recent accessions.

PENNSYLVANIA

PHILADELPHIA

409 Pennsylvania Railroad Company, General Office Library, 20th
Floor, Suburban Station Bldg., 1617 Pennsylvania Blvd.,
zone 4.
   Miss E. M. Ferguson, Librarian.
   Areas: the 13 states served by the railroad.
   Subjects: transportation.
   Size: map sheets 77; atlases 144 vol.
   Serves organization. Iln., commercial phst.

410 Philadelphia City Planning Commission, Land Planning Division.
   Lucile T. Caldwell, Planning Librarian.
   A large collection of maps drawn in the Division. Not
   available for loan.

411 Temple Univ. Library, zone 22.
   Size: map sheets 150; atlases 40 vol.
   Serves students' needs in connection with courses in history
   geography, political science, literature.

PITTSBURGH

412 Bureau of Mines, (U.S.) Central Experiment Station, Topo-
graphic Map Collection, 4800 Forbes St., zone 13.
   Marion L. Hatch, Librarian.
   Mrs. Margaret B. Parker, Library Assistant.
   Staff: 1 p-t.
   Areas: United States, Latin America.
   Subjects: geology, coal resources, oil and gas, mineral
   resources.
   Size: map sheets - all USGS topographic maps and folios
   and some others.
   Serves organization and public. Iln.

413 Carnegie Free Library of Allegheny, Federal and Ohio Sts.,
zone 12.
   Eva Abrams, Reference Librarian.
   Areas: United States, Pennsylvania, Pittsburgh and sur-
   rounding counties.
   Size: atlases 25 vol.; globes 1.
   Serves public.

PENNSYLVANIA

PITTSBURGH

4   Carnegie Museum, 4400 Forbes St., zone 13.
Specialists available: geographers, translators, explorers,
biogeographers, biologists.
Areas: worldwide.
Subjects: animal and plant distribution, archeology.
Size: map sheets 5,000 (including USGS quadrangles);
atlases 50 vol., 25 titles; globes 6; models 10; air
photos, several dozen.
Serves research and exhibition needs of Carnegie Museum.
Iln., phst., photo. No centralized collection, Museum
Library and individual sections have map collections.
Sections have built up working collections of maps for
geographic areas of interest. Bird Section, for example,
has many maps of Latin American countries, a few of which
may be unusual. Mammal Section has various maps of Arctic
America. In general, Carnegie Museum scientists start
with available maps and superimpose data derived from
their own studies of plant, animal, and human distribution;
for example, the Upper Ohio Valley Archeological Survey
has located over 500 Indian sites in tri-state areas in
past three years. County maps and drainage maps of such
distribution will be included in the final report of the
Survey.
Publications: Annals.

15 The Historical Society of Western Pennsylvania, 4338 Bigelow
Blvd., zone 13.
F. F. Holbrook, Librarian.
Areas: Pittsburgh and parts of western Pennsylvania, to-
gether with adjacent areas in neighboring states.
Subjects: local and regional history, genealogy.
Size: map sheets 275; atlases 30 vol., 30 titles; globes
1; models 1.
Serves public. Iln.; commercial reproductions only; exch.
Publications: acquisitions are reported currently in the
quarterly, Western Pennsylvania Historical Magazine,
vol. 1, 1918 - .

PENNSYLVANIA

PITTSBURGH

416   Univ. of Pittsburgh Library, zone 13.
       Gertrude M. Kneil, Assistant, Reference Dept.
       Staff: 2 p-t; specialists available: geographers,
         translators.
       Areas: worldwide.
       Size: map sheets 10,000; atlases 105 vol., 86 titles.
       Serves faculty, students, public. AMS depository.

STATE COLLEGE

417   Pennsylvania State College, Pattee Library.
       Mrs. Ruby M. Miller.
       Staff: 1 p-t; specialists available: geographers, carto-
         graphers, translators.
       Areas: western and central Europe, United States,
         Pennsylvania.
       Subjects: city planning, topography, transportation,
         agriculture, geology.
       Size: map sheets 35,000; atlases 88 vol., 66 titles;
         globes 3.
       Serves faculty, students, public. Phst., exch.
       Publications: The Headlight, new series, no. 1, June
         1951 -

SWARTHMORE

418   Swarthmore College Library.
       Howard H. Williams, Readers Service Librarian.
       Size: map sheets 350 (includes geologic folios); atlases
         70 vol., 50 titles; globes 1.
       Serves college and Delaware County in a limited way. Iln.,
         commercial phst. and micro., exch. Sproul Observatory
         has celestial maps and photos.

WILLIAMSPORT

419   James V. Brown Library, 19 E. Fourth St.
       Catharine T. Shulenberger, Reference Librarian.
       Staff: 2 p-t.
       Areas: general collection with separate grouping of state
         and local material.

PENNSYLVANIA

419 (continued)
      Size: map sheets 1,005; est. 2,000 not counted or
      cataloged; atlases 30 vol., 24 titles; globes 1.
      Serves public. Commercial reproductions only.

PUERTO RICO

RIO PIEDRAS

420 University Library, Map Room (proposed).
      Mrs. Sarah C. Diaz Latimer, Library Assistant.
      Areas: worldwide.
      Size: map sheets 30,000. AMS depository.

RHODE ISLAND

KINGSTON

421 Univ. of Rhode Island.
      Staff: 1 p-t; specialists available: geographers.
      Areas: Rhode Island.
      Size: map sheets 60,000; atlases 50 vol.
      Serves faculty, students, public. Iln., phst., photo.,
      exch.

NEWPORT

422 Newport Historical Society, 82 Touro St.
      Herbert O. Brigham, Librarian.
      Areas: Rhode Island, Newport County.
      Serves public. Iln., phst., photo., commercial only;
      exch.

423 Redwood Library and Athenaeum.
      Donald T. Gibbs, Librarian.
      Areas: New England, majority are 19th Century.
      Size: map sheets 293; atlases 120 vol., 107 titles;
      globes 2.
      Serves public. Phst. and photo., commercial only.

RHODE ISLAND

NEWPORT

424 U.S. Naval War College.
        Cdr. J.C. Bentley, USN, Chart Room Officer.
        Staff: 1; cartographers available.
        Areas: worldwide.
        Subjects: aeronautical, hydrography, military geography.
        Size: map sheets 10,000; atlases 225 vol., 52 titles;
           globes 100; models, few.
        Serves staff and students.   Photo., blueprinting.

PROVIDENCE

425 Brown Univ., zone 12.
        Staff: 1 p-t.
        Size: map sheets 24,000; atlases not est.
        Serves univ. and public.   Iln., phst., photo., micro.,
           depository for U.S. Army and U.S. Coast and Geodetic
           Survey; part housed in main library and part in Geology
           Dept.

426 Providence Public Library, 229 Washington St., zone 2.
        Areas: East Coast, Rhode Island.
        Subjects: local history, Civil War (Fiske-Harris collection)
        Size: map sheets 7,500; atlases 115 vol., 95 titles.
        Serves public.   Iln. within Providence area, phst., photo.,
           Contura, exch.

427 Rhode Island Historical Society, 52 Power St., zone 6.
        Clifford P. Monahon, Librarian.
        Specialists available: faculty of Brown Univ.
        Areas: Rhode Island.
        Size: map sheets 400; atlases 60 vol.
        Serves public.   Iln., phst., photo., micro., exch.
        Publications: Chapin, Howard Millar. Cartography of Rhode
           Island. Providence, 1915. 9 p.____. Checklist of
           maps of Rhode Island. Providence, Preston & Rounds,
           1918. 48 p.

SOUTH CAROLINA

CLEMSON

428   Clemson College Library.
       Mrs. R. W. Rutledge, Librarian for Archives.
       Staff: 1 p-t; specialists available: cartographers,
         geographers, translators, faculty.
       Size: map sheets 27,000.
       Serves college and public. Phst., AMS depository
         completely cataloged.

SOUTH DAKOTA

PIERRE

429   South Dakota State Historical Society, Memorial Bldg.
       Will G. Robinson, Secretary.
       Areas: west of the Mississippi and north of Kansas River
         to Rocky Mountains.
       Subjects: local history, soils, geology, resources.
       Size: map sheets 600; atlases 60 vol.; models 2; air
         photos 25.
       Serves society and public. Photo., exch.
       Publications: The Wi-iyohi, Monthly Bulletin of the South
         Dakota Historical Society.

430   State Highway Commission, Highway Planning Survey, Capitol
       Bldg.
       Leo W. Fargen, State Manager.
       Staff: 2 p-t; specialists available: geographers, carto-
         graphers, translators.
       Areas: South Dakota.
       Subjects: transportation.
       Size: map sheets 89; air photos - partial state coverage.
       Serves organization and public. Iln., black and white
         prints. Maps are available for reference and for sale.

TENNESSEE

CHATTANOOGA

Tennessee Valley Authority. See 431.

TENNESSEE

KNOXVILLE

431   Tennessee Valley Authority, Central Map and Drawing Services,
      102-A Union Bldg.
         Benton McKeehan, Office Engineer.
         (Branch Office: 105 Pound Bldg., Chattanooga, Paul Klyce,
         Office Engineer.)
         Staff: 12 in Knoxville; 6 in Chattanooga; specialists
         available: cartographers.
         Areas: Tennessee Valley region.
         Subjects: planimetry, topography, water navigation, flood
         control, power.
         Size: map sheets 10,000 (excluding map stocks); atlases
         250 vol.; air photos 25,000.
         Serves organization, government agencies, public. Phst.,
         photo., blueprint, white print, and other reproductions.
         Restricted to TVA material.   Subject to security regula-
         tions.   Library service for engineering records is sup-
         plied all Divisions of the Authority.   This service is
         also available to the public in connection with maps and
         other engineering data.   The organization is the official
         agency for the sale of all TVA maps, charts, and graphic
         material, including reproductions.   The collection in-
         cludes several hundred thousand original drawings made
         for the planning, design, and construction of the
         Authority's hydroelectric and steam-electric power
         projects.
         Publications: (List of Maps, Charts, and Reproductions
         Available.)
         Reproductions available: Valley Topographic Mapping.
         Index to Quadrangles. Navigation Charts: Reproductions
         Available as of July 1, 1952. Explanation of Numbering
         System.

432   Univ. of Tennessee, Dept. of Geology-Geography Library.
         Robert G. Long, Assistant Professor.
         Staff: 2 p-t; specialists available: geographers, carto-
         graphers, faculty, staffs of State and U.S. Geological
         Surveys.
         Areas: Latin America, Tennessee Valley.
         Subjects: topography.

TENNESSEE

32 (continued)
Size: map sheets 15,000; atlases 10 vol., 10 titles;
globes 12; mounted wall maps 450; models 6; air photos,
few.
Serves students, faculty, public. Iln., Apeco photo-
copier for small maps, exch.

MEMPHIS

33 Cossitt Library, 33 S. Front St., zone 3.
C. Moffett Moore, Head of Reference Dept.
Areas: United States, Tennessee, Memphis.
Subjects: topography, geology, local history.
Size: map sheets 236, plus official soil, topographic
and transportation maps of United States and maps of
the alluvial valley of the Mississippi River; atlases
100 vol., 75 titles, plus 224 geologic atlases; globes 1.
Serves public. Commercial reproductions, exch. In addition, many folded city plans are in regular information
file.

NASHVILLE

34 Joint University Libraries, Peabody College, Scarritt College,
Vanderbilt Univ., zone 4.
A. F. Kuhlman, Director.
Depository for AMS and USGS maps.

35 Tennessee State Planning Commission, Greyhound Terminal
Bldg., 517 Commerce St., zone 3.
Lillian Brower, Librarian.
Staff: 1 p-t; specialists available: geographers, geologists.
Areas: Tennessee.
Subjects: population, transportation, navigation, topography,
city planning, zoning.
Size: map sheets 2,000; atlases 4 vol., 3 titles.
Serves organization and public. Multilith for 9x14 in. max.
As a public service a number of state maps are available
for distribution.

TEXAS

AUSTIN

436 Univ. of Texas, Map Collection.
Ella Mae Bridges.
Staff: 4 p-t; specialists available: geographers, trans-
lators, Bureau of Economic Geology.
Areas: Latin America, southern United States, Texas.
Subjects: history, geology.
Size: map sheets 64,410; atlases 925 vol., 850 titles.
Serves faculty, students, public. Iln., phst.

BEAUMONT

437 Tyrrell Public Library, Pearl & Forsythe Sts.
Mrs. Dorothy Yezak, Reference Librarian.
Staff: 1.
Size: map sheets 334; atlases 48 vol., 48 titles;
globes 4.
Serves public. Phst., photo.

COLLEGE STATION

438 Texas A & M College, Dept. of Oceanography, Personal Library
of W. Armstrong Price, Geologist and Oceanographer.
Staff: 1 p-t; specialists available: geologists, oceano-
graphers.
Areas: Gulf of Mexico, Texas.
Subjects: geology, cartographic history, topography,
coasts.
Size: map sheets 500; atlases 15 vol., 15 titles; air
photos 50.
Serves graduate students in oceanography and geology, research of self and students. Phst., photo., ozalid, micro.

439 Texas A & M College Library.
Dorothy Churchwell, Circulation Librarian.
Areas: Southwest United States.
Subjects: geology, weather.
Size: map sheets 305; atlases 230 vol.; globes 2.
Serves faculty, students, public. Iln.

TEXAS

COLLEGE STATION

440 Texas Engineers ,Library.
     Robert E. Betts, Librarian.
     Specialists available: geographers, geologist.
     Areas: southwestern United States, Texas.
     Subjects: geology, petroleum, highways.
     Size: map sheets 774; atlases 6 vol., 6 titles; globes 2.
     Serves registered professional engineers of the state,
          faculty and students of Engineering School of Texas A &
          M College, staff of the Engineering Experiment Station,
          public. Iln (atlases only), phst.

COMMERCE

441 East Texas State Teachers College Library.
     Lora E. Smith, Reference Librarian.
     Specialists available: geographers.
     Subjects: history, transportation.
     Size: map sheets 60; atlases 10-20 vol.; globes 1 and
          others in history and geography classrooms; 400 regional
          air charts of world.
     Serves students.

CORPUS CHRISTI

442 La Retama Public Library, 511 S. Broadway.
     Edith Cosgrove, Reference Librarian.
     Size: map sheets 100 (mostly National Geographic);
          atlases 18 vol., 18 titles; globes 1.
     Serves public. Iln.

DALLAS

443 Southern Methodist Univ., Fondren Library, Map Library, zone 5.
     Eleanor Maclay, Map Librarian.
     Staff: 1; specialists available: geographers.
     Areas: western Europe, Latin America, southwestern United
          States, Texas.
     Subjects: geology, soils, topography, oil and gas resources,
          transportation.

TEXAS

443 (continued)
Size: map sheets 76,000; atlases 15 vol., 15 titles;
globes 1; air photos 2,056.
Serves faculty, students, public. Iln., exch.

DENTON

444 North Texas State College Library.
Areas: Southwestern United States.
Subjects: history, petroleum.
Size: map sheets 589; atlases 69 vol.; globes 2.
Serves college. Iln., can reproduce up to 10"x14".

EL PASO

445 Texas Western College Library.
Mrs. Miriam C. Patton, Reference Librarian.
Staff: 1; specialists available: geographers, carto-
graphers, translators.
Areas: west Texas and New Mexico.
Subjects: geology.
Size: map sheets 702; atlases 20 vol., 18 titles; globes
1; air photos 27.
Serves faculty, students, public. Most of the maps are
used by the Geology and Military Science Depts. and
are kept in those depts.

GALVESTON

446 Rosenberg Library, 823 Tremont St.
Mildred Stevenson, Reference Librarian.
Staff: 2 p-t.
Areas: Gulf region of Texas, Galveston.
Subjects: local history.
Size: map sheets 5,250; atlases 25 vol.; globes 1.
Serves public. Collection includes topographic quad-
rangles and pilot charts published by United States
government.

TEXAS

HOUSTON

447 Gulf Publishing Company Library, Post Office Box 2608, zone 1.
Mary N. Zuber, Librarian.
Staff: 1; specialists available: translators.
Areas; worldwide.
Subjects: petroleum, geology.
Serves organization. Iln., phst., exch.
Publications: World Oil, Annual Publication - July 15,
each year; World Oil Atlas of Petroleum.

448 Houston Public Library, 500 McKinney.
Staff: 1 p-t.
Areas: Houston.
Subjects: geology, local history.
Size: map sheets 700; atlases 70 vol., 55 titles; globes 1.
Serves public.

449 Rice Institute, Fondren Library.
Helen Chillman.
Staff: 1 p-t, specialists available: translators,
faculty.
Areas: southern United States, Texas.
Subjects: American history, local history, geology.
Size: map sheets 30,000; atlases 60 titles; globes 2.
Serves faculty, students, local research laboratories
(oil, geology). Iln., atlases only; photo., commercial
phst.; exch. AMS depository.

450 Univ. of Houston Libraries, Cullen Blvd., zone 4.
Howard F. McGaw, Director.
Size: map sheets 253; atlases 26 vol., 26 titles; globes
2; hundreds of maps in offices and classrooms on campus.
Serves community. Iln., photo., exch. A central inven-
tory of maps is planned.

SAN ANTONIO

451 San Antonio Public Library, 210 W. Market St.
Map collection limited to general maps available in pro-
portion to the Library's needs.

UTAH

LOGAN

452 Utah State Agricultural College, Claypool Map Library, Box 97.
Mrs. Mary C. Edwards, Claypool Map Librarian.
Staff: 2 p-t; specialists available: geographers, geologist
Areas: North America.
Subjects: geology, physical geography, agriculture.
Size: map sheets 13,240; atlases 18 vol., 18 titles;
globes 4; models 4; air photos 28.
Serves faculty, students, public. Also contains approxi-
mately 1,500 vol. in fields of cartography and geology,
and a vertical file.
Publications: feature article in the Salt Lake Tribune,
autumn, 1951.

PROVO

453 Brigham Young Univ. Library.
Samuel Chandler, Assistant Librarian in charge of Science
Library.
Staff: 3 p-t.
Areas: United States and Utah.
Subjects: meteorology.
Size: map sheets 33,000; atlases 250 vol.; globes 3;
models 2.
Serves faculty, students, public. Photo., exch.

SALT LAKE CITY

454 State Road Commission, 442 State Capitol.
Gerald Matthews, Chief Planning Engineer.
Maintains a private map file for reference sources based on
Utah map coverage from various agencies such as General
Land Office; township plats; aerial photographs obtained
through the Soil Conservation Service. Publishes various
state, city, and county maps which are available to the
public at a nominal charge.

UTAH

SALT LAKE CITY

455   Univ. of Utah Library.
      Edith Rich, Engineering Librarian.
      Staff: 2 p-t; specialists available: geographers, geo-
         logists.
      Areas: Rocky Mountains, Utah.
      Subjects: geological, topographical.
      Size: map sheets 25,000; atlases 36 vol., 15 titles
         (includes 220 geological atlases bound in 22 vol.);
         globes 1.
      Serves faculty, students, public, military and naval
         units on campus and at Fort Douglas. Commercial re-
         productions only, exch. AMS depository.

VERMONT

BURLINGTON

456   Univ. of Vermont Libraries.
      Staff: p-t.
      Areas: New England, with emphasis on Vermont.
      Subjects: local history.
      Size: map sheets 1,500; atlases 25 vol.; globes 1;
         models 1.
      Serves organization and public. Iln., phst. The Univ.
         Library has a small collection of topographic maps and
         geologic folios of New England primarily but of the
         United States in general. In the historical Vermont
         Library attempt is made to have a good historical col-
         lection of atlases and wall maps.

VIRGINIA

HOPEWELL

457   Maude Langhorne Nelson Library.
      Size: map sheets 63; atlases 11 vol.; globes 1.
      Serves public. Iln.

VIRGINIA

NEWPORT NEWS

458 The Mariners' Museum Library.
     John L. Lochhead, Librarian.
     Staff: 1 p-t.
     Areas: worldwide, Virginia, Maryland, North Carolina.
     Subjects: waterways, navigation, transportation,
       hydrographic.
     Size: map sheets 1,553; atlases 150 vol., 125 titles;
       globes 4.
     Serves organization and public. Photo., commercial phst.
     Library also has a collection of charts.
     Publications: map collection is described in the museum's
       History and Guide.

459 Newport News Shipbuilding and Dry Dock Co., 4101 Washington
     Ave.
     Areas: United States, Virginia.
     Subjects: transportation, water power.
     Size: map sheets 100; atlases 20 vol., 6 titles; air
       photos, few.
     Serves organization. Iln., phst., photo., blueprint,
       ozalid, vandyke, micro.; exch.

NORFOLK

460 Norfolk Museum of Arts and Sciences, Yarmouth St.
     Mrs. W. F. Thompson.
     Staff: p-t; specialists available: cartographers.
     Areas: eastern Virginia and North Carolina, tidewater
       section of Virginia.
     Size: map sheets 100.
     Serves public. Phst., photo.

PORTSMOUTH

461 Norfolk Naval Shipyard Museum.
     Marshall W. Butt, Curator.
     Staff: 2 p-t; specialists available: local historian.
     Areas: Portsmouth, Norfolk, Norfolk County, Hampton Roads.
     Subjects: local history.
     Size: map sheets 100 (chiefly phst.)

VIRGINIA

461 (continued)
Serves organization and public. Iln. except copies under
glass, phst., exch. For historical and exhibit purposes
the Shipyard Museum collects maps of the local area
where the Shipyard is located. It wishes to obtain
phst. of maps of Norfolk, Portsmouth, Gosport, Norfolk
County, and the lower Hampton Roads region, especially
those antedating 1925.

RICHMOND

462 Virginia Dept. of Highways, 1221 E. Broad St.,
A. H. Bell, Location and Design Engineer.
Staff: 6; specialists available: cartographers.
Areas: Virginia.
Subjects: transportation.
Size: map sheets 118 (county maps); atlases 1 vol.
Serves organization, government agencies, and the public.
Phst., photo., black on white or blue prints. County
maps are sold at $10. per atlas; state highway maps
are free.

463 Virginia State Library.
Staff: 1 p-t.
Areas: Virginia.
Subjects: local history.
Size: map sheets 5,000 (exclusive of AMS depository);
atlases 50 vol.
Serves organization. Phst., photo.
Publications: Maps Relating to Virginia . . . Virginia
State Library Bulletin, 1914.

WASHINGTON

CHENEY

464 Eastern Washington College of Education, Dept. of Geography
and Geology.
Areas: United States, Pacific, Europe, Asia.
Size: map sheets 8,000-10,000. Scattered collection including USGS and AMS surplus. For teaching and laboratory study.

WASHINGTON

CHENEY

465 Eastern Washington College of Education, Hargreaves Library,
     Maps are part of the Northwest History collection.
       C. S. Kingston, Professor Emeritus of History.
       Staff: 1; 1 p-t; specialists available: geographers.
       Areas: Washington, Oregon, Idaho, Montana.
       Subjects: local history.
       Size: map sheets 200; atlases 50 vol.; globes 1.
       Serves college and community. Iln. for atlases.

ELLENSBURG

466 Central Washington College of Education, Social Science
     Division.
       R. S. Funderburk, Associate Professor of Geography.
       Staff: 1 p-t.
       Areas: Pacific Northwest.
       Subjects: physical.
       Size: map sheets 500; globes 5; models 6.
       Serves college and local community. Collection is designed
         primarily for instructional purposes.

OLYMPIA

467 State Capitol Historical Association, 211 W. 21st St.
       Ida N. Burford, Curator-Director.
       Serves public. Reproductions arranged through the State
         Museum.

468 Washington State Highway Dept., Highway Planning Division.
       C. K. Glaze, Planning Engineer.
       Staff: (map drafting) 12; specialists available: carto-
         graphers.
       Areas: Washington, Oregon, Idaho.
       Subjects: transportation, traffic.
       Serves organization and public. Phst., offset. The Dept.
         prepared maps of the counties of Washington, scales 1 in.
         equals 1 mile and 1/2 in. equals 1 mile. Sets of these
         maps serve the organization and are available to the
         public at a nominal price.

WASHINGTON

SEATTLE

469 Edward W. Allen, private collector, 3711 48th Ave., N.E.
     Areas: north Pacific coast of America, also Japan.
     Subjects: historical geography.
     Size: map sheets 400; atlases 50 vol.; globes 1.
       Collection has been exhibited in the Seattle Public
       Library, Seattle Art Museum, Seattle Museum of History
       and Industry, and the Univ. of Washington.

470 Univ. of Washington, Fisheries and Oceanography Library,
     203 Fisheries Center, zone 5.
       Staff: 1 p-t.
       Areas: ocean coasts.
       Subjects: navigation, oceanography.
       Size: map sheets 800; atlases 10 vol., 10 titles; air
         photos 4.
       Serves organization and public. Iln., phst., photo.,
         micro., exch.

471 Univ. of Washington Library,
     J. Ronald Todd, Chief Reference Librarian.
       Areas: Oregon, Washington, Idaho, Montana, British Col—
         umbia, Alaska.
       Subjects: geology, history.
       Size: map sheets 13,435; atlases 472 vol., 422 titles;
         globes 2.
       Serves faculty, students, public. Iln., phst., photo.,
         micro.

TACOMA

472 Metsker Maps, Charles F. Metsker, Cartographer, 111 S. 10th
     St., zone 2.
       Publisher of maps and atlases of Washington, Oregon, Idaho,
         and California. Dealer in maps, atlases, globes.

473 Tacoma Public Library, 1102 S. Tacoma Ave.
       Areas: United States, Washington, Pierce County, Tacoma
         and vicinity.
       Subjects: geology, local history.

WASHINGTON

473 (continued)
Size: map sheets 10,350; atlases 73 vol., 66 titles;
globes 1.
Serves public. Phst. General and historical maps are in
the History Division, technical maps are in the Business
and Technology Dept. The library is a partial depository for U.S. government documents.

474 Washington State Historical Society Library, 315 Stadium Way.
Alta F. West, Librarian.
Areas: Pacific Northwest.
Subjects: history.
Size: map sheets 600; atlases 15 vol.
Serves public. Commercial phst. and photo.

WEST VIRGINIA

CHARLESTON

475 State Road Commission, Planning Division, Library, Room 224,
State Office Bldg. no. 3.
C. A. Rothrock, State Planning Engineer.
Staff: 1.
Areas: West Virginia.
Subjects: highways, traffic flow.
Size: map sheets 200; air photos, state-wide coverage.
Serves organization and public. Maps published by the
Commission are for sale to the public.

MORGANTOWN

476 West Virginia Univ., Library, Map Room.
Barbara C. Burhans, Jr., Reference Librarian.
Staff: 2 p-t; specialists available: geographers,
cartographers.
Areas: West Virginia, Virginia before 1863.
Subjects: topography, local history.
Size: map sheets 41,000.
Serves faculty, students, public. Phst., photo., micro.,
Contura, exch. An additional collection of maps is
housed in the west Virginia Collection which specializes
in state and local history.

WEST VIRGINIA

MOUNDSVILLE

77 Delf Norona, private collector, 315 Seventh St.
    Areas: Early West Virginia, Virginia, maps drawn by Indians
      of North America.
    Subjects: history.

WISCONSIN

BELOIT

78 Beloit College Libraries.
    Melville R. Spence, Assistant Director.
    Staff: 1 p-t; specialists available: geographers, carto-
      graphers, translators.
    Size: map sheets 18,000; atlases 45 vol., 42 titles;
      globes 2; air photos 25.
    Serves faculty and students. Iln., Collection is mainly
      AMS depository.

KENOSHA

79 Kenosha County Historical Museum, County Court House.
    Carrie Cropley, Curator.
    Staff: 1 p-t.
    Areas: Wisconsin, Kenosha.
    Subjects: state and local history.
    Size: map sheets 60; atlases 25 vol.
    Serves public. Phst.

MADISON

80 State Historical Society of Wisconsin, 816 State St., zone 6.
    Josephine L. Harper, Manuscript and Map Librarian.
    Staff: 2; 1 p-t; specialists available: geographers,
      cartographers.
    Areas: North America (early, 16th-18th Centuries),
      United States, Wisconsin.
    Subjects: history, topography, transportation, agriculture,
      local history.
    Size: map sheets 11,000; atlases 1,200 vol., 1,200 titles.

WISCONSIN

480   (continued)
Serves Univ. of Wisconsin and public. Phst., photo., exch.
Maps are cataloged by author, area, and subjects within
area; atlases are cataloged by author and area. All atlases prior to 1800 and a few of later date have been
analyzed and the individual maps cataloged. Entire collection is shelflisted.

481   Univ. of Wisconsin, Map Library, Room 322, Science Hall.
Arthur H. Robinson, Professor of Geography.
Staff: 1; specialists available: geographers, cartographers
Areas: worldwide.
Size: map sheets 80,000; air photos 25,000.
Serves the Univ. and public. Iln., exch. Atlases are held
in the Geology and Geography Library.

MILWAUKEE

482   Milwaukee Public Library, 814 W. Wisconsin Ave., zone 3.
Mrs. Esther G. Hamilton, Acting Chief, Reference Dept.
Areas: worldwide, United States, Wisconsin, Milwaukee.
Subjects: local history, soils, topography, geology.
Size: map sheets 45,000; atlases 350 vol.; globes 1;
models 2.
Serves public. Iln., phst., photo., exch. Depository
for AMS and USGS. Majority of maps in Reference Dept.;
smaller collections developed and serviced in subject
depts.

OSHKOSH

483   George P. Nevitt, private collector, P.O. Box 360.
Areas: Wisconsin and the Great Northwest Territory.
Size: atlases 2 vol., map sheets 120; Iln., exch.

484   Oshkosh Public Museum, 785 Algoma Blvd.
Specialist available: James E. Lundsted, Curator of
Anthropology, Fox-Wolf River valley area.
Areas: Fox-Wolf River valleys, Winnebago County, Oshkosh.
Subjects: local history.
Size: map sheets 20; atlases 5 vol.; models 1; air
photos 25.

WISCONSIN

484 (continued)
Serves public. Photos, 35mm negatives, exch. The Museum
has taken over the files and activities of the former
Winnebago Historical and Archeological Society.

485 State College, Geography Dept.
L. M. Bradbury.
Specialists Available: geographers.
Areas: United States, Wisconsin.
Subjects: geology and geography.
Size: map sheets 2,500; atlases 100 vol., 20 titles;
globes 25; air photos, selected areas.
Serves college. Phst. Maps and atlases have been selected
for class and laboratory purposes, not for research or
as an extensive collection.

RACINE

486 Racine Public Library.
Edward B. Hayward, Librarian.
Areas: United States, Wisconsin.
Subjects: transportation, topography, geology.
Size: map sheets, not. est. (includes U.S. Public Roads
Administration maps, USGS quadrangles for Wisconsin,
USGS geologic atlas of United States, International
Boundary maps, Lake Survey charts); atlases 55 vol.,
45 titles.
Serves public. Iln.

WAUKESHA

487 Waukesha County Historical Society, Court House.
Mrs. E. Tallmadge, Custodian.
Areas: Wisconsin, Waukesha County and city.
Subjects: local history.
Size: map sheets 70; atlases 13 vol.
Serves public. Phst.

WYOMING

CHEYENNE

488 Wyoming Highway Dept., Planning Division, State Office Bldg.
   W. A. Gallup, Planning Engineer.
   Staff: 3.
   Areas: Wyoming.
   Subjects: transportation.
   Size: map sheets 32.
   Serves the Highway Dept. Iln., phst., blueprints. Copies
   furnished free.

489 Wyoming State Archives and Historical Dept., State Office Bldg
   Lola M. Homsher, Director.
   Areas: Wyoming and the Rocky Mountain West.
   Subjects: western history.
   Size: small, not yet cataloged.
   Serves public. Commercial reproductions only, exch.

LARAMIE

490 Univ. of Wyoming Library.
   N. O. Rush, Director.
   Mrs. Lois Payson, Acting Director.
   Staff: 1 p-t; specialists available: translators, geology
   dept. faculty.
   Areas: Rocky Mountain region, Wyoming.
   Subjects: geology, local history.
   Size: map sheets not est., includes AMS, USGS, and USDA
   depositories; atlases 56 vol., 47 titles; globes 1.
   Serves faculty, students, citizens of Wyoming, Iln., phst.

ALBERTA, CANADA

EDMONTON

491 Dept. of Lands and Forests, Technical Division, 6th Floor
   Administration Bldg., No. 1.
   H. Soley.
   Staff: 1; 1 p-t; specialists available: cartographers,
   aerial photograph analysts.
   Areas: Canada, Alberta.

ALBERTA, CANADA

91 (continued)
    Subjects; topographic and planimetric maps.
    Size: map sheets 3,700 (including 3,100 township plans);
    atlases 6 vol.; air photos 155,775.
    Serves public. Phst., photo., ozalid, exch. Price lists
    available.

BRITISH COLUMBIA, CANADA

VANCOUVER

92 Univ. of British Columbia, Dept. of Geography and Geology,
    zone 8.
    J. Lewis Robinson, Chairman, Geography Division.
    Staff: 1; specialists available: geographers, cartographers.
    Areas: northwest Europe, British Colonial Africa, Canada,
    British Columbia.
    Subjects· geomorphology of Canada.
    Size: map sheets 6,000; atlases 15 vol.; globes 5; models
    12; air photos 500.
    Serves students and faculty. Collection includes complete
    sets of government maps of Canada and British Columbia.

92a Univ. of British Columbia Library, zone 8.
    Doreen Taylor, Junior Librarian.
    Staff: 1 p-t; specialists available: geographers, carto-
    graphers, translators.
    Areas: Canada, British Columbia, western and central Europe.
    Historical maps of British Columbia are part of the Howey-
    Reid Collection of Canadiana.
    Subjects: topography, geology, planning.
    Size: map sheets 18,000; atlases 100 vol.
    Serves faculty, students, public. Iln., phst., micro.,
    exch. Map and atlas collection almost complete cataloged
    by the Boggs-Lewis system.

BRITISH COLUMBIA, CANADA

VICTORIA

493 Geographic Division, Dept. of Lands and Forests, Parliament
Bldgs.
W. H. Hutchinson, Chief, Geographic Division.
Staff: 29; specialists available: geographers, carto-
graphers, surveyors, photogrammetrists, soil and water-
rights engineers.
Areas: British Columbia.
Subjects: topographic and cadastral surveys.
Size: map sheets 45,000; air photos 350,000.
Serves organization and public. Phst., ozalid, litho-
graph. Not a library in the true sense, for the Divi-
sion compiles, produces, and distributes maps of British
Columbia. The Air Photo Library maintains a very full
coverage of air photos of British Columbia for sale or
loan.

MANITOBA, CANADA

WINNIPEG

494 Provincial Library of Manitoba, Legislative Bldg.
Marjorie Morley.
Staff: 1 p-t; specialists available: members of the Geo-
graphical Society of Manitoba.
Areas: Canada.
Subjects: topography, transportation, fur trade, geopolitics
Size: map sheets 4,000.
Serves government departments and public. Iln. for maps only

495 Univ. of Manitoba Library.
Arthur E. Millward, Map Librarian.
Staff: 1 p-t; specialists available: geographers, trans-
lators, faculty.
Areas: Canada.
Size: map sheets 1,500; atlases 30 vol.
Serves faculty, students, and public. Iln.

496 Winnipeg Public Library.
A. F. Jamieson, Chief Librarian.
Areas: Canada.
Size: map sheets 400; atlases 37 vol.
Serves public.

NEWFOUNDLAND, CANADA

ST. JOHN'S

497 Dept. of Mines and Resources.
Primarily stocks maps produced by the Dept. for sale and
distribution, but maintains a photograph library of
100,000 aerial photos of Newfoundland.

ONTARIO, CANADA

HAMILTON

498 Hamilton College, McMaster Univ., Map Library, Dept. of
Geography.
L. G. Reeds, Chairman, Dept. of Geography.
Staff: 2 p-t; specialists available: geographers, carto-
graphers.
Areas: western Europe, Latin America, United States, Canada.
Subjects: topography, land use.
Size: map sheets 15,000; atlases 100 vol.; globes 50;
models 25; air photos 1,000.
Serves faculty and students.

OTTAWA

499 Geographical Branch, Dept. of Mines & Technical Surveys,
Map Library Division, Room 100, Elgin Bldg., 74 Elgin St.
E. L. Burkholder, Jr., Map Librarian.
Staff: 3; 4 p-t; specialists available: geographers,
cartographers, translators.
Areas: worldwide with emphasis on Canada.
Subjects: various.
Size: map sheets 175,000; atlases 200; globes 5; models
(plastic) 20; air photos 15,000; ground photos 10,000.
Serves organization and public. Iln., phst., photo.,
exch. Collection almost completely indexed and
cataloged according to the Boggs system.
Publications: Map Library Accession Lists.

ONTARIO, CANADA

OTTAWA

500 Geological Survey of Canada, Library, National Museum Bldg.,
     zone 4.
     Robert Shanks, Assistant Librarian.
     Staff: 1 p-t; specialists available: cartographers.
     Areas: Canada, Great Britain, United States.
     Subjects: geology, topography.
     Size: map sheets 25,000; atlases 100 vol.; globes 1.
     Serves organization. Iln., exch.
     Publications: Ferrier, W. F. Annotated Catalogue of &
        Guide to Publications of the Geological Survey, 1845-
        1917. Leafloor, L. Publications of the Geological
        Survey of Canada, 1917-1952.

501 Ottawa Public Library, 114 Metcalfe St.
     Elizabeth L. Hunter, Reference Librarian.
     Staff: 2 p-t.
     Areas: Canada, Ontario, Quebec.
     Subjects: topography.
     Size: map sheets 950; atlases 50 vol., 40 titles.
     Serves public.

502 National Air Photo Library, Dept. of Mines and Technical
     Surveys.
     E. J. Meek.
     Areas: Canada (coverage almost 100 percent).
     Size: 3,000,000 air photos; prints available.
     Serves government and public.

503 Public Archives of Canada, Map Division, Sussex St.
     A. J. H. Richardson, Chief, Map Division.
     Staff: 5; specialists available: historians.
     Areas: worldwide, Canada, Mississippi Valley, Arctic,
        Alaska, Greenland.
     Subjects: various.
     Size: map sheets 22,000; atlases 400 vol., titles 350;
        models 5.
     Serves public. Phst., exch.
     Publications: Holmden, H.R. Catalogue of Maps, Plans,
        and Charts in the Map Room of the Dominion Archives.
        Ottawa, 1912. New edition in preparation.

ONTARIO, CANADA

OTTAWA

504   Univ. of Ottawa, Library.
Auguste-M. Morisset, O.M.I., Librarian.
Dr. T. Jost, Chairman, Geography Dept.
Specialists available: geographers, cartographers,
translators, faculty.
Areas: worldwide, Canada, United States.
Subjects: morphology, economics.
Size: map sheets 15,000; atlases 15 vol.; models 50;
globes 1.
Serves faculty, students, public. Iln., exch.

TORONTO

505   Dept. of Lands and Forests, Division of Surveys and Engi-
neering, Map Distribution and Surveys Records Office,
Provincial Air Photographic Library, Parliament Buildings.
F. W. Beatty, Surveyor General of Ontario and Chief,
Division of Surveys and Engineering.
W. E. Carroll, in charge of map collections.
Staff: 1; 4 p-t; specialists available: geographers,
cartographers, surveyors.
Areas: Canada, Ontario.
Subjects: ground surveying and some local history, survey plans of roads, railways, subdivisions, floodings,
power lines, mining locations, base and meridian lines,
lake and river traverses, explorations.
Size: map sheets (survey plans) 15,000; field notebooks
3,500; other volumes 350; atlases 10 vol.; air photos
52,000.
Serves government depts., surveyors, public. Phst., dry
process reproductions. Office distributes copies of all
maps published by the Dept. of Lands and Forests, of the
Province of Ontario, as shown on its form S 39, the Dept.
of Mines and Technical Surveys, Ottawa, as shown on form
S 40, as well as the maps produced by the Dept. of National Defence, Ottawa,, and distributed through the Dept. of
Mines and Technical Surveys. The collection of survey
records, plans and field notes is in the process of being
catalogued by area, surveyor and date.

ONTARIO, CANADA

TORONTO

506 Alexander E. MacDonald, private collector, 488 Huron St.,
    zone 5.
    Areas: America, Great Lakes, Canada, Toronto.
    Subjects: discovery, early cartography of the Great
    Lakes, local mapping, especially 16th, 17th and 18th
    Centuries.
    Size: map sheets 300. Phst. This private collection
    has been built up as a hobby over 30 years and in-
    cludes maps by Mercator, Jansson, Le Testu, Maffei,
    Visscher, Rosario.

507 Toronto Public Library, Reference Division, College & St.
    George Sts., zone 2-B.
    Staff: 1 p-t.
    Areas: Canada, Ontario, Toronto.
    Subjects: local history, topography, geology.
    Size: map sheets 4,500; atlases 118 vol., 101 titles.
    Serves public. Iln. only within Canada, micro. Maps
    issued with government reports, books, and periodicals
    are cataloged with them, and not analyzed as maps.
    Publications: Map Collection of the Public Reference
    Library of the City of Toronto, Toronto, 1923.

QUEBEC, CANADA

MONTREAL

507a McGill Univ., Dept. of Geography.
    Collection for teaching purposes.

508 Municipal Library of Montreal, 1210 Sherbrooke St. East,
    zone 24.
    Areas: Canada, New France including Louisiana, United
    States.
    Subjects: history of French Canada.
    Size: map sheets 500.
    Serves public.

QUEBEC, CANADA

MONTREAL

509 Univ. of Montreal, Central Library, C.P. 6128.
     Bernard Chouinard and Marcel Tiphane.
     Staff: 2; specialists available: geographers, carto-
        graphers, translators.
     Areas: Canada, Quebec.
     Subjects: geological, mineral.
     Size: map sheets 16,000; atlases 350 vol.; globes 4;
        models 35; air photos 800.
     Serves faculty and students. Iln., exch.

510 Univ. of Montreal, Dept. of Geography, 2900 Mount Royal
     Blvd., zone 26.
     Bernard Chouinard, Curator.
     Staff: 1; specialists available: geographers, carto-
        graphers, translators.
     Areas: Province of Quebec.
     Size: map sheets 5,000; atlases 100 titles; models 12;
        air photos 500.
     Serves faculty and students. Iln., exch.

511 Univ. of Montreal, Game and Fisheries Dept., Biological
     Bureau Library, D' 634, 2900 Mount Royal Blvd., zone 26.
     Camille Vallee, Librarian.
     Staff: 2; 2 p-t; specialists available: geographers,
        cartographers, translators, biologists, lake inspectors.
     Areas: waters of the world, Canada, Quebec.
     Subjects: world water systems, biogeography, distribution
        of organisms, vegetation, soils.
     Size: map sheets 2,500; atlases 6 vol.; air photos 1,000.
     Serves univ. and Quebec Biological Bureau. Iln., phst.,
        photo., offset, multilith; exch. Drawing staff available.

QUEBEC

512 Archives de la Province, Plains of Abraham.
     Areas: Canada, Province of Quebec.
     Subjects: history of the Province of Quebec.
     Size: map sheets 900; atlases 40 vol.; models 3.
     Serves organization and public. Iln., phst., photo.,
        exch. Collection includes the Atlantic Neptune.

QUEBEC

513 Dept. of Lands and Forests, Surveys and Cadastral Branches,
     Government Bldg.
     Georges Cote, Director of Surveys.
     Staff: 5; specialists available: cartographers,
        translators.
     Areas: Canada, Quebec.
     Subjects: boundaries of electoral districts, municipal
        counties, fish and game reserves, railroads.
     Size: map sheets 160.
     Serves organization and public. Exch., maps for sale.
     Publications: List of Maps published by Surveys Branch.

514 Laval Univ., Archives.
     Rev. H. Provost, Assistant Archivist.
     Staff: 2; specialists available: historians.
     Areas: North America, Canada, Quebec.
     Subjects: North American and local history.
     Size: map sheets 1,900; atlases 156 titles.
     Serves faculty, students, public. Iln. for atlases only,
        phst., micro., exch.

515 Laval University, Cartotheque of the Dept. of Geology,
     Library D, Faculty of Sciences, Blvd. de l'Entente.
     Carl Faessler, Professor of Mineralogy.
     Staff: 1; 2 p-t; specialists available: geologists.
     Areas: Canada.
     Subjects: topography and geology.
     Size: map sheets 3,000; atlases 400.
     Serves faculty, students, public. Iln., phst., exch.
     Thousands of maps published with annual reports, memoirs,
        and professional papers are bound with the text and kept
        in the Library.

516 Laval Univ., Institute of Geography and History.
     Jean-Marie Roy, Professor of Geography.
     Areas: worldwide, Canada.
     Size: map sheets 15,000; atlases 125 vol., 125 titles;
        globes 1.
     Serves faculty, students, public. Iln.; the Faculty of
        Forestry has a collection of air photos.

SASKATCHEWAN, CANADA

REGINA

517 Dept. of Mineral Resources, Administration Bldg.
      J. Toews, Engineer Assistant.
      Staff: 5; specialists available: geologists, petroleum
        engineers.
      Areas: Saskatchewan.
      Subjects: geology, mineral rights.
      Serves organization and public. Phst., blueprints,
        maps for sale.

SASKATOON

518 Univ. of Saskatchewan Library.
      Miss M.R. Murray, Reference Librarian.
      Staff: 1 p-t.
      Areas: Canada.
      Size: map sheets 300; atlases 85 vol.
      Serves faculty and students.

THE LIBRARY OF CONGRESS

WASHINGTON 25, D. C.

MAP RESOURCES COMMITTEE

REFERENCE DEPARTMENT
MAP DIVISION

Executive Members:
Maud D. Cole
Kathleen Irish
Dorothy C. Lewis
Joseph W. Rogers
Marie C. Goodman, Chairman

Advisory Members:
Nathaniel Abelson
George R. Dalphin
Alexander O. Vietor
Bill M. Woods
Ena L. Yonge

Dear Sir:

   In cooperation with the Special Libraries Association, the Library of Congress is preparing an inventory of map library resources of the United States and Canada. This volume will supplement the reference work entitled <u>Special Library Resources</u>.

   The purpose of this communication is to request information on the map and atlas resources of your library for inclusion in this new compilation.

   Sample entries are shown on the back of this letter to illustrate the format in which we plan to present the information.

   Inasmuch as the index will be based largely on answers to questions 8 and 9, we hope you will give them special attention.

   Your cooperation in filling out the enclosed entry form carefully and returning it within ten days will be greatly appreciated. A self-addressed envelope which requires no postage is enclosed for your convenience and an extra copy of the questionnaire is included for your files.

Cordially yours,

Marie C. Goodman

(Mrs.) Marie C. Goodman
Chairman
Map Resources Committee

APPENDIX I

1. Name of library or organization:
2. Special name of map collection, if any:
3. Address:
4. Name and title of person in charge of maps:
5. Number of persons employed in map collection: Full time_____
                                                  Part time_____
6. Are specialists available for consultation? Yes_____ No_____
                                  Geographers   _____ _____
                                  Cartographers   _____ _____
                                  Translators   _____ _____
                                  Others (explain)_____ _____
7. On what areas does the map collections specialize? (For ex-
    ample, Chicago, Ohio, Canada, U.S.S.R., Latin America,
    Pacific Ocean)
8. On what subjects does the map collection specialize? (For ex-
    ample, geology, local history, transportation)
9. Size of map collection:
      Approximate number of map sheets_____
      Approximate number of atlases   _____
                    i.e., volumes _____ separate titles_____
      Globes   _____
      Relief models   _____
      air photographs   _____
10. What group does the map collection serve?
      Organization   _____
      Public   _____
      Other (explain)   _____
11. Are maps and atlases available on interlibrary loan? Yes___
                                                          No___
      If yes, under what conditions?
12. What reproduction facilities are available?
      Photostats   _____
      Photographs   _____
      Other   _____
13. Are you interested in exchanging maps and atlases with other
    libraries? Yes_____ No_____
      Conditions:
14. Cite any publications about your collection:
15. Please list the names and addresses of any private map collec-
    tions in your area which might not be known to the committee:
16. Use space below for any qualification or extension of the
    above answers that may be necessary or for significant points
    not covered by the questions:

APPENDIX II

United States Government Map Depositories
A = Army Map Service
G - Geologic maps of the U.S. Geological
  Survey
T = Topographic maps of the U.S. Geo-
  logical Survey
Alabama Polytechnic Institute   A
  Auburn, Alabama
State Teachers College   A
  Florence, Alabama
University of Alabama Library   AGT
  University, Alabama
University of Alaska, College, Alaska   A
Librarian, Dept. of Library & Archives   T
  309 State House, Phoenix, Arizona
University of Arizona Library   AGT
  Tucson, Arizona
University of Arkansas   AGT
  Fayetteville, Arkansas
Arkansas Geological Survey   G
  Little Rock, Arkansas
University of California Library   AGT
  Berkeley 4, California
Claremont Colleges Library   AGT
  Claremont, California
Fresno State College   A
  Fresno 4, California
Scripps Institution of Oceanography   T
  La Jolla, California
Los Angeles Public Library   AGT
  Los Angeles 13, California
Los Angeles City College   A
  Los Angeles 27, California
University of Southern California   AG
  Los Angeles 7, California
University of California Library   AGT
  Los Angeles 24, California
Oakland Public Library   AT
  Oakland, California
California Institute of Technology   GT
  Pasadena, California
California State Library   T
  Sacramento, California
Stanford University, Stanford, Calif.   AGT
San Diego Public Library   AT
  San Diego 1, California
California Academy of Sciences Library   AGT
  Golden Gate Park, San Francisco 18,
  California
Div. of Mines   GT
  St. Dept. of Natural Res., San
  Francisco 11, California
San Francisco Public Library   T
  San Francisco 2, California
McGill University Library   GT
  Montreal, Canada
Deputy Director of Military Survey   A
  Army Survey Establishment, RCE
  Department of National Defense
  Ottawa, Canada
Geological Survey of Canada   GT
  Ottawa, Ontario, Canada
University of Colorado Libraries   AGT
  Boulder, Colorado
Colorado College, Colorado Springs, Colo.   GT
Fountain Valley School   A
  Colorado Springs, Colorado
Denver Public Library, Denver 2, Colo.   AGT

Bureau of Mines Library   GT
  214 New Customhouse, Denver 2, Colo.
U.S. Geological Survey   GT
  Denver Federal Center, Denver 14, Colo.
Curator of Map Library   A
  University of Denver, Denver 10, Colo.
Colorado School of Mines   AGT
  Golden, Colorado
Bridgeport Public Library   AT
  Bridgeport 4, Connecticut
Connecticut State Library   AT
  Hartford 1, Connecticut
Public Library, Hartford, Conn.   T
Connecticut Geological Survey   T
  Trinity College, Hartford 6, Conn.
Wesleyan University   AGT
  Middletown, Connecticut
Public Library, New Haven, Conn.   T
Yale University, New Haven, Conn.   AGT
University of Connecticut   AGT
  Storrs, Connecticut
State Highway Dept., Dover, Delaware   G
Wilmington Institute Free Library   T
  Wilmington, Delaware
The Catholic University of America   AGT
  Washington 17, D.C.
Georgetown University Library   AGT
  Washington 7, D.C.
George Washington University   A
  Washington 6, D.C.
Howard University, Washington 1, D.C.   G
Library of Congress   AGT
  Washington 25, D.C.
National Geographic Society   AT
  16th & M Streets, N.W., Washington 6, D.C.
University of Florida   AT
  Gainesville, Florida
University of Miami, Miami, Florida   A
Florida Geological Survey   GT
  Tallahassee, Florida
Florida State University   AT
  Tallahassee, Florida
University of Georgia Libraries   AGT
  Athens, Georgia
Dept. of Mines, Mining & Geology   GT
  State Capitol, Atlanta, Ga.
Georgia Institute of Technology   A
  Atlanta, Georgia
Georgia Historical Society   T
  501 Whitaker St., Savannah, Georgia
University of Hawaii, Honolulu, Hawaii   A
University of Idaho Library   AGT
  Moscow, Idaho
Idaho State College, Pocatello, Idaho   AT
Public Library, Aurora, Illinois   T
Southern Illinois University   AGT
  Carbondale, Illinois
Eastern Illinois State College   A
  Charleston, Illinois
Chicago Public Library, Chicago 2, Ill.   T
Chicago Natural History Museum   AT
  Roosevelt Road and Lake Shore Drive
  Chicago 5, Illinois
Field Museum of Natural History   G
  Chicago, Illinois
Map Library, University of Chicago   AGT
  Chicago 37, Illinois
John Crerar Library, Chicago 1, Ill.   T

Newberry Library, Chicago 10, Ill. ´AT
Gail Borden Public Library   T
  Elgin, Illinois
Northwestern University   AGT
  Evanston, Illinois
Monmouth College Library   A
  Monmouth, Illinois
Illinois State Normal Univ.   A
  Normal, Illinois
Bradley University, Peoria 5, Ill.   A
Public Library, Peoria, Illinois   T
Augustana College Library   A
  Rock Island, Illinois
Illinois State Library   AT
  Springfield, Illinois
University of Illinois Library   AGT
  Urbana, Illinois
State Geological Survey Division   GT
  100 Natural Resources Bldg.
  Urbana, Illinois
Wheaton College Map Collection   A
  Wheaton, Illinois
Indiana University, Bloomington, Ind. AGT
Wabash College, Crawfordsville, Ind.   T
De Pauw University, Greencastle, Ind.   GT
Dept. of Conservation   G
  Division of Oil & Gas
  311 W. Washington St.,
  Indianapolis, Ind.
State Library   AGT
  140 N. Senate, Indianapolis 4, Indiana
Purdue University, Lafayette, Indiana AT
Librarian, Public Library   AT
  Lafayette, Indiana
University of Notre Dame   GT
  Notre Dame, Indiana
Valparaiso University   A
  Valparaiso, Indiana
Iowa State College, Ames, Iowa   T
State Highway Commission, Ames, Iowa   T
Public Library, Burlington, Iowa   T
Coe College, Cedar Rapids, Iowa   T
Public Library, Council Bluffs, Iowa   T
Davenport Public Museum   T
  Davenport, Iowa
Public Library, Des Moines 9, Iowa   A
State Traveling Library   T
  Des Moines 19, Iowa
Carnegie-Stout Free Public Library   T
  Dubuque, Iowa
State University of Iowa Libraries   AGT
  Iowa City, Iowa
Iowa Geological Survey   T
  103 Geology Bldg., Iowa City, Iowa
University of Kansas Library   AGT
  Lawrence, Kansas
Bethany College, Lindsburg, Kansas   A
Kansas State College   GT
  Manhattan, Kansas
Kansas State Library, Topeka, Kansas   T
State Historical Society   T
  Memorial Bldg., Topeka, Kansas
Covington Public Library   A
  Covington, Kentucky
University of Kentucky Library   AGT
  Lexington 29, Kentucky
Louisiana State University   AGT
  Baton Rouge 3, Louisiana
Howard-Tilton Mem. Libr., Tulane Univ.   T
  New Orleans 18, Louisiana

New Orleans Public Library   T
  New Orleans 13, Louisiana
Public Library, Bangor, Maine   T
Bowdoin College, Brunswick, Maine   AT
Bates College, Lewiston, Maine   T
University of Maine, Orono, Maine   AGT
Public Library, Portland, Maine   T
Colby College, Waterville, Maine   AT
The Johns Hopkins University   AGT
  Baltimore 18, Maryland
Enoch Pratt Free Library   AGT
  Baltimore 1, Maryland
Peabody Institute   T
  Mount Vermont Place, Baltimore, Md.
University of Maryland   A
  College Park, Maryland
Amherst College Library   AGT
  Amherst, Massachusetts
Appalachian Mountain Club   T
  3 Joy Street, Boston, Massachusetts
Babson Institute, Babson Park 57, Mass.   T
Boston Athenaeum, Boston 8, Mass.   T
Boston Public Library   AT
  Boston 17, Massachusetts
Boston Society of Civil Engineers   T
  715 Tremont Temple, Boston, Mass.
Massachusetts State Library   T
  State House, Boston, Massachusetts
Harvard College Library   AGT
  Cambridge, Massachusetts
Massachusetts Institute of Technology   AGT
  Cambridge 39, Massachusetts
Haverhill Public Library   T
  Haverhill, Massachusetts
Tufts College, Medford, Mass.   T
Free Public Library   T
  New Bedford, Massachusetts
Smith College, Northampton, Mass.   AGT
Essex Institute, Salem, Mass.   T
Mount Holyoke College   GT
  South Hadley, Massachusetts
City Library Association   T
  Springfield, Massachusetts
Wellesley College   ACT
  Wellesley 81, Massachusetts
Williams College   T
  Williamstown, Massachusetts
Clark University Library   AT
  Worcester 3, Massachusetts
Free Public Library, Worcester, Mass.   T
University of Michigan   AGT
  Ann Arbor, Michigan
Detroit Public Library   AGT
  5201 Woodward Avenue, Detroit 2, Mich.
Wayne University, Detroit 1, Michigan   T
Michigan State College   A
  East Lansing, Michigan
Michigan College of Mining and
Technology Library   AGT
  Houghton, Michigan
Western Michigan College Library   A
  Kalamazoo, Michigan
Michigan Geological Survey   T
  Lansing, Michigan
Michigan State Normal College   A
  Ypsilanti, Michigan
St. Johns University Library   A
  Collegeville, Minnesota
Duluth Public Library   AT
  Duluth 2, Minnesota

Minnesota Geological Survey   GT
  Minneapolis, Minnesota
Public Library, Minneapolis, Minn.   T
University of Minnesota   GT
  Minneapolis, Minnesota
Carleton College, Northfield, Minn.   AT
St. Olaf College, Northfield, Minn.   A
James Jerome Hill Reference Library   GT
  St. Paul 2, Minnesota
Minnesota Historical Society   T
  St. Paul, Minnesota
St. Paul Public Library   A
  St. Paul 2, Minnesota
Gustavus Adolphus College   A
  St. Peter, Minnesota
Mississippi State College   GT
  St. College, Mississippi
Mississippi Geological Survey   GT
  University, Mississippi
University of Mississippi   T
  University, Mississippi
Mississippi River Commission   T
  P.O. Box 80, Vicksburg, Miss.
University of Missouri   AGT
  Columbia, Missouri
Kansas City Public Library   AT
  Kansas City 6, Missouri
Linda Hall Library   AGT
  5109 Cherry Street
  Kansas City 4, Missouri
Missouri School of Mines, Rolla, Mo.   AGT
Mo. Geological Survey & Water Resources T
  P.O. Box 250, Rolla, Missouri
Academy of Science of St. Louis   T
  4642 Lindell Blvd., St. Louis 8, Mo.
Washington University   AGT
  St. Louis 5, Missouri
St. Louis Public Library   AT
  St. Louis 3, Missouri
St. Louis University   AGT
  3621 Olive Street, St. Louis, Mo.
U.S.A.F. Aeronaut. Chart & Info. Center T
  Att: ACDL, Second & Arsenal Sts.,
  St. Louis 18, Missouri
Montana State College Library   T
  Bozeman, Montana
Montana School of Mines, Butte, Mont.   AGT
Montana State University   A
  Missoula, Montana
State Library, Lincoln 9, Nebr.   T
University of Nebraska   AGT
  Lincoln 8, Nebraska
Public Library, Omaha, Nebraska   T
Nevada State Library   AT
  Carson City, Nevada
University of Nevada, Reno, Nevada   AGT
State Library, Concord, N.H.   T
University of New Hampshire Library   GT
  Durham, New Hampshire
Dartmouth College, Hanover, N.H.   AGT
Librarian, Manchester City Library   T
  Manchester, New Hampshire
Upsala College, East Orange, N.J.   A
Free Public Library, Elizabeth, N.J.   T
Rutgers University Library   AGT
  New Brunswick, New Jersey
Free Public Library, Newark, N.J.   T
Princeton University Library   AGT
  Princeton, New Jersey

Bureau of Geology & Topography   GT
  Dept. of Conservation & Econ. Devel.
  520 E. State St., Trenton 9, N. J.
State Teachers College   A
  Trenton 5, New Jersey
University of New Mexico Library   AG
  Albuquerque, New Mexico
N. Mex. Bureau of Mines & Mineral Res.   GT
  Socorro, New Mexico
New York State Library, Albany, N.Y.   AT
New York State Museum, Albany, N.Y.   GT
Brooklyn College, Brooklyn 10, N.Y.   T
Brooklyn Public Library   AT
  Grand Army Plaza, Brooklyn 17, N.Y.
Pratt Institute Library   T
  Brooklyn 5, New York
Buffalo Public Library, Buffalo 3, N.Y.   AT
University of Buffalo, Buffalo, N.Y.   A
Grosvenor Library, Buffalo, N.Y.   T
Hamilton College Library   G
  Clinton, New York
Harpur College, Endicott, N.Y.   GT
Colgate University Library   A
  Hamilton, New York
Cornell University, Ithaca, N.Y.   AGT
American Geographical Society   AGT
  Broadway at 156th Street
  New York 32, New York
American Museum of Natural History   GT
  77th St. & Eighth Ave., New York, N.Y.
Geology Library   AT
  Columbia University, New York 27, N.Y.
Cooper Union, New York, N.Y.   T
Engineering Societies Library   GT
  29 W. 33rd St., New York 18, N.Y.
New York Historical Society   T
  170 Central Park West, New York, N.Y.
New York Public Library   AT
  New York 18, New York
Library of New York University
  New York 53, New York
School of Asiatic Studies   A
  The Asia Institute, 7 East 70th Street
  New York 21, New York
Hartwick College, Oneonta, New York   A
Vassar College, Poughkeepsie, N.Y.   GT
University of Rochester   GT
  Rochester, New York
Union College, Schenectady, N.Y.   T
Syracuse University Library   AGT
  Syracuse 10, New York
Rensselaer Polytechnic Institute   T
  Troy, New York
United States Military Academy   G
  West Point, New York
University of North Carolina Library   AGT
  Chapel Hill, North Carolina
Duke University, Durham, N.C.   A
Dept. of Conservation & Development   GT
  Div. of Mineral Resources
  P.O. Box 2719, Raleigh, N.C.
State Library, Raleigh, North Carolina   T
Wake Forest College Library   AT
  Wake Forest, North Carolina
North Dakota Agricultural College   AGT
  Fargo, North Dakota
University of North Dakota   AGT
  Grandforks, North Dakota
State Teachers College, Valley City, N.D.   A

ublic Library, Akron, Ohio   T
ept. of Geography and Geology   A
  Bowling Green State University
  Bowling Green, Ohio
niversity of Cincinnati   AGT
  Cincinnati 21, Ohio
ublic Library, Cincinnati 2, Ohio   AT
ase Institute of Technology   GT
  10900 Euclid Ave., Cleveland 6, Ohio
estern Reserve University Libraries   AGT
  1111 Euclid Avenue, Cleveland 6, Ohio
leveland Museum of Natural History   T
  2717 Euclid Ave., Cleveland 15, Ohio
leveland Public Library   AT
  325 Superior Avenue, Cleveland 14, Ohio
he Ohio State University Library   AGT
  Columbus 10, Ohio
ayton Public Library   AT
  215 E. Third Street, Dayton 2, Ohio
hio Wesleyan University, Delaware, Ohio   T
enyon College, Gambier, Ohio   T
enison University, Granville, Ohio   T
ent State University Library   AT
  Kent, Ohio
arietta College, Marietta, Ohio   AT
berlin College, Oberlin, Ohio   AT
iami University, Oxford, Ohio   A
arder Public Library   T
  Springfield, Ohio
oledo Public Library   AT
  325 Michigan Street, Toledo 2, Ohio
niversity of Toledo   AT
  2801 West Bancroft Street, Toledo 12, Ohio
ntioch College Library   AGT
  Yellow Springs, Ohio
ublic Library of Youngstown &
ahoning County   T
  Youngstown, Ohio
niversity of Oklahoma   AGT
  Norman, Oklahoma
klahoma State Library   A
  109 State Capitol, Oklahoma City 5, Okla.
klahoma Agricultural and Mech. School   AGT
  Stillwater, Oklahoma
ulsa Public Library, Tulsa, Okla.   T
niversity of Tulsa, Tulsa 4, Okla.   A
regon State College, Corvallis, Oregon   AT
he University of Oregon Library   AGT
  Eugene, Oregon
State Dept. of Geology & Min. Ind.   G
  702 Woodlark Bldg., Portland 5, Oregon
Library Assoc. of Portland   T
  801 S.W. 10th Avenue, Portland 5, Oregon
regon State Library, Salem, Oregon   AT
uhlenburg College, Allentown, Penna.   A
ryn Mawr College Library   AGT
  Bryn Mawr, Pennsylvania
ickinson College, Carlisle, Penna.   T
afayette College, Easton, Penna.   GT
ureau of Topographic & Geol. Survey   G
  Dept. of Internal Affairs
  Harrisburg, Pennsylvania
averford College, Haverford, Penna.   T
Bucknell University Library   A
  Lewisburg, Pennsylvania
Academy of Natural Sciences of Phila.   GT
  Logan Square, Philadelphia, Penna.
Franklin Institute   T
  Parkway at 20th Street
  Philadelphia 3, Pennsylvania

The Free Library of Philadelphia   AT
  Logan Square, Philadelphia 3, Penna.
Temple University   T
  Sullivan Memorial Library
  Philadelphia 22, Pennsylvania
University of Pennsylvania   T
  Philadelphia, Pennsylvania
Carnegie Free Library of Allegheny   T
  Federal & Ohio Streets, Pittsburgh 12, Pa.
Carnegie Library, Pittsburgh, Penna.   GT
U.S. Bureau of Mines Library   GT
  4800 Forbes St., Pittsburgh, Penna.
University of Pittsburgh Library   AG
  Map Division, Pittsburgh, Pennsylvania
Public Library, Scranton 10, Penna.   T
State Teachers College Library   A
  Shippensburg, Pennsylvania
State Teachers College   A
  Slippery Rock, Pennsylvania
Lehigh University   GT
  South Bethlehem, Pennsylvania
The Pennsylvania State College   AGT
  State College, Pennsylvania
Osterhout Free Library   T
  71 So. Franklin, Wilkes-Barre, Penna.
University of Puerto Rico   A
  Rio Piedras, Puerto Rico
State College Library   A
  Kingston, Rhode Island
Naval War College, Newport, R.I.   G
Athenaeum Library   T
  251 Benefit St., Providence, R.I.
Brown University Library   AGT
  Providence 12, Rhode Island
Librarian, Providence Public Library   T
  Providence, Rhode Island
Rhode Island State Library   T
  Providence, Rhode Island
Clemson College, Clemson, S.C.   A
University of South Carolina   AGT
  Columbia 19, South Carolina
Furman University, Greenville, S.C.   T
South Dakota State Agricultural College   AT
  Brookings, South Dakota
S. Dak. Sch. of Mines & Technology   G
  Rapid City, South Dakota
State Geological Survey   GT
  Vermillion, South Dakota
University of Tennessee   AGT
  Knoxville 16, Tennessee
Memphis State College, Memphis, Tenn.   A
Cossitt Library, Memphis 3, Tennessee   T
Joint University Libraries   A
  Nashville 4, Tennessee
Tennessee Dept. of Conservation   T
  Div. of Geology, G-5 State Office Bldg.,
  Nashville, Tennessee
Tennessee State Library   AT
  Nashville 3, Tennessee
Vanderbilt University   GT
  Nashville 4, Tennessee
The University of Texas, Austin, Texas   AGT
Texas State Library   AT
  State Capitol, Austin, Texas
West Texas State Teachers College   A
  Station 1, Canyon, Texas
Dallas Public Library, Dallas 1, Texas   AT
Southern Methodist University   AGT
  Dallas 5, Texas
Coll. of Mines & Metallurgy, El Paso, Tex.   A

Fort Worth Public Library   A
  Fort Worth, Texas
Houston Public Library, Houston, Texas   T
The Rice Institute Library   AG
  Houston 1, Texas
Texas Technological College   GT
  Lubbock, Texas
Baylor University Library   AT
  Waco, Texas
Utah Agricultural College   T
  Logan City, Utah
University of Utah Library   AGT
  Salt Lake City 1, Utah
Librarian, Free Library   T
  Brattleboro, Vermont
University of Vermont   GT
  Burlington, Vermont
Middlebury College, Middlebury, Vt.   AT
State Library, Montpelier, Vermont   T
Norwich University, Northfield, Vt.   T
Virginia Polytechnical Institute   T
  Blacksburg, Virginia
Bridgewater College, Bridgewater, Va.   T
University of Virginia   AGT
  Charlottesville, Virginia
Hampden-Sidney College   T
  Hampden-Sidney, Virginia
Virginia Military Institute   T
  Lexington, Virginia

Virginia State Library   AT
  Richmond 19, Virginia
Washington State Library   T
  Olympia, Washington
State College of Washington   AT
  Pullman, Washington
Seattle Public Library   AT
  Seattle 4, Washington
University of Washington   AGT
  Seattle 5, Washington
College of Puget Sound   T
  Tacoma, Washington
Tacoma Public Library, Tacoma, Wash.   T
State of W.Va., Dept. of Archives
  & History   T
  State Capitol, Charleston, W.Va.
West Virginia University Library   AGT
  Morgantown, West Virginia
Beloit College Libraries   AGT
  Beloit, Wisconsin
University of Wisconsin   AGT
  Madison 6, Wisconsin
Wisconsin State Historical Society   T
  816 State St., Madison 6, Wisc.
Milwaukee Public Library   AT
  814 West Wisconsin Avenue
  Milwaukee 3, Wisconsin
University of Wyoming   AGT
  Laramie, Wyoming